Coketown
Barney Farmer

Illustrations by Lee Healey

Drunken Baker
Coketown

ISBN 978-1-9031106-8-3

First published in this edition 2019 by Wrecking Ball Press.

Illustrations by Lee Healey

Book design by humandesign.co.uk

To blazes.

Duke of Wellington,
Iron Duke of lore,
put guns on these streets,
eight strikers on the floor,
including two boys,
17, 19.
Four died.
Both boys.
Obscene.
Back to front.
If only Napoleon
had killed the cunt.

John Mercer, 27
William Lancaster, 25
George Sowerbutts, 19
Bernard McNamara, 17
August 13th, 1842.

'The Clair Street protest in August 1842 has been called both a riot and a massacre. It was prompted by cotton workers calling for better wages and by Chartist campaigners seeking greater civil rights for working people. When protesters gathered on Clair Street they were met by local soldiers. In the following stand-off, the troops fired shots which ricocheted off buildings and killed four of the protesters.'

Troops fired shots which ricocheted off buildings and killed four.

Shots which ricocheted off buildings and killed.

Shots ricocheted.

Ricocheted.

Ricocheted.

Ricocheted is a lie.

An official lie, that extract above, hanging on the wall in a grand public pile.

A newly apparent absence of malice, a twist of fate, oh wicked chance, such cruel luck.

Look what happened, not what was done, what simply occurred.

Has been called both a riot and a massacre.

Has been called.

Riot and massacre.

Former by killer,

latter by survivor.

Another grey area softly absolving those who pulled triggers, who ordered triggers pulled, who placed trigger-pullers in this town on that street that night.

Placed in towns countywide, to be fair.

To deal with strikes, meet the strikers,

when and where required.

The Duke had a whisper in Peel's ear,

smells of revolution over Lancashire...

Local soldiers, ours, though, see above, but then we had the big barracks so –

Needful context, maybe, half a story never being less than a lie of omission.

A perfunctory passage performing cosmetic surgery on a permanent scar in this town's perfidious bastion of Victorian enlightenment.

A mendacious edifice, as we shall see, as I shall *show*, this neo-classical giant pledged to rational inquiry, sworn by words etched into its own stone flesh.

Letters the width and height of that imposing pediment,

a hundred feet above the square,

loom o'er our head, the shoppers, the cidermen,

Cenotaph, benches and surrounding pavement.

'To Literature, Arts and Science.'

Under these fine words from on high do seekers of truth and learning and what survives of the record library approach great pillars of the community, each reaching

high as the Satanic stacks of Jerusalem, wide at their widest as a cow is long.
Paragon of that muscle architecture brought home from the Grand Tour.
Structure of empire built by empire-builders, eminent power, gravity, density, into which humbled citizens shuffle, each aware this epic arrangement of earthly matter will outlast them and all they know.
That traces will endure, a stumpy cornerstone juts, a shattered column stands,
when the sun swells to sweep away our work, as waves wipe wormcasts from sands.
Enter and ascend, a staircase either side, matching, sweeping, broad.
Pass arts and crafts of the modest civic haul,
pass lost men of war picked out in black on gold,
to gain first floor landing and great round hall.
Four storeys storing stories, those chosen told.
From the circular first floor gallery, at the flat stone rim, glance left then right to local history then records, gaze up to art, look down on literature, the lending library and beyond, the computer suite, where jobseekers jump through benefit hoops and the odd pensioner settles odd accounts on machines booked solid for millennia.
Human precision graces every plane, every clean sandstone edge, every curved rail, every sharply defined cornice, the patient work of hands and minds long dust.
A Foucault pendulum, 120ft ceiling to near floor, cleaves space to and fro and around we all go, our brief rotating span nearer end upon each completed arc.
At night, when the doors are closed, it swings in the dark.
Back on floor one turn left and pass through the big double-door to learn about this town.
To gain the potted tale, follow the agreed trail from cro-magnon hut and big elk bones to village begat marketplace, and on, to rain and river borne Cottonopolis.
Great men and benefactors, great leaps forward on the onward blindfold march.
And of this town's moment on the frontline?
That early industrial stint at the epicentre of a soon-to-be global struggle, then new-born, crying out, now dying, old, the pitting of flesh against gold.
Of when Karl Marx put the case of this town's people to an audience in the New World.
Of Dickens, of Hard Times and Coketown, of this town's *reel* story.
The story of why the people in this town are here, of the ghosts in this town's spinning machine, of the threads binding this town's present and future to a distant night of riots and ricochets, protest and massacre, four bodies in the ground.
Nameless men, as our edifice of Enlightenment tells it, chanced to be shot on the cobbles.
And nameless boys.
And the wounded, what word of them? Silence.
Silent as capricious bullets, as targeted violence.

1

Made a start.

A prologue.

Or preface.

Introduction?

Happy whatever, numerically.

Four dozen stretches that length you've got a thickish book.

Got to hit the archives. Bit of research. Not too much. Some to hide behind, some to knowingly disregard. You need to know what you mean to ignore.

Got to stand up that Duke of Wellington bit at least.

Set out to shitdaub a national hero, even an idiot's hero, *especially* an idiot's hero, you've got to bring the goods. One amateur local historian website last updated 2002 does not constitute firm ground.

Who knows what axe that fucker had to grind?

Could've been a Bennite. A flat-out Communist. A 1970s power-crazed union agitator nursing a grudge against the high-born, keen to keep abreast of the information super-highway with a view to disseminating skewed views.

Logged off a decade and more ago, either given up or round the twist or under sod or so much scattered gritty ash.

Gritty ash.

Where Diddymen go to die.

Remember that, not bad.

Enemies within, sire, hissed the evil Duke in the Prime Minister's ear, fiendishly twirling his moustache. His own moustache not the Prime Minister's.

Did either man have a moustache?

He was on the fiver for pity's sake. There'll be burly men with his likeness tattooed on their skin.

Now it's Churchill. Same sort of cunt, another sworn enemy of the working class.

Loosed soldiers against your fellow citizens?

This could be your ticket to fiver eminence.

Maybe one of the Bloody Sunday killers next up for the honour?

Their commanding officer did get knighted post bloody murder.

But how does Dickens tie into this, or this into he?

He was on the fiver for pity's sake.

He was on a tenner. Bumped Florence Nightingale.

Bastards on fivers, angels on tenners.

Well, not angels. Barnaby Rudge is some evil shite.

Starts brilliant but then you want to thump Rudge on sight.

Many of Dickens' heroes are punchable by today's standards.

Wilde was right about Little Nell. Overjoyed when she finally croaked.

Need him further up. First line, first word, Dickens, Hard Times, Coketown, this town, conspiracy, this is what we're talking about.

You got 800 words on a totally different strike, killings and ricochets a dozen year before the bastard even rocked up.

Wonder if he knew?

Possible not.

No statue until 1992.

How common was the knowledge?

How was the story told and by who?

Hour on the microfiche will clear all that up, and much much more.

He'd've known. He was woke. He was engaged. Course he'd've fucking known. Yet no mention in Hard Times. Unless I missed it.

On balance, don't yank that thread. Whatever the case it doesn't mean this town isn't Coketown, but it'll prick the suspicions of dickheads.

Don't give succour to thick and cynical people you want to buy the book, Barney.

You'll be admitting Coketown is an amalgam of several towns, ingredients in a rich soup, this town being the cauldron, that's enough.

Why dish out sticks to twat your book in the prologue?

Preface.

Introduction.

More Dickens sooner, that half-arsed nod in the last few par reads like an afterthought.

It was an afterthought. Be honest with yourself from the start.

Is there really a book in this?

Yes there is. And if I wasn't heading out I'd be in and on it.

No need to go insane. Few extra paragraphs, spell it out plain.

This town makes nothing of the fact it is widely understood to have been the principle inspiration for Coketown. Why? Why are other significant events in this town's political history now being remastered and remixed?

This not unique, is universal. Governed, groomed by the governing, the patient work of hands and minds over centuries, guiding a narrative, balancing our past.

And "ricocheted" is the local arm of this process baring its arse in public.

A cognitive step too far.

They've slipped up. I've caught the lying sods.

The physics implausible, the word jars aloud.

Eight wounds, eight ricochets, what are the odds?

Obviously better when shooting at a crowd.

Should be jotting this down. Sticking it in my phone.

And blah blah blah, so too since long ago and up until today is the truth of Coketown, the town that is mostly this town, ruthlessly managed...

Managed out of sight

Out of sight out of mind is their game.

No plaque, no statue, no mark, no claim.

A pisspoor caricature on the wall of the tunnel which led once to the stables of the hotel now duff pub where I'll drink my last tonight, at which the storyteller crashed January 1854, halfway through the seven month strike.

Two months later, first of April, first of Hard Times in Household Words.

Sold like hot free sex cakes, doubled mag sales, Dickens' biggest commercial and critical success to date.

Two days prior Karl Marx put this town on the front of the New York Tribune, urging all with an interest in the elevation of labour to support our workers.

A defining author of his age.

A defining thinker of our epoch.

This town.

The Great Author, a century dust but still raking in tourist bucks across the land, blue plaques and visitor centres, souvenirs to take home and treasure a lifetime. The Great Author who set one novel wholly outside London, who took one foray North, to a Lancashire milltown convulsed by industrial unrest, to Coketown, a fictional parish founded mostly, not totally, not going to claim that, just mainly, on events and accounts seen and recorded in this town.

And yet nothing.

Heritage catnip and sweet fuck all.

Why?

Don't kid me towns like this town don't routinely dip their bread on thinner grounds, don't sop up thinner gruel. Bury St Edmunds wanks itself daft over one line in Pickwick.

Don't tell me Hard Times tours, events, street theatre, all that shite and a lottery-funded bronze-effect life-size Dickens statue idiots can stand next to and have their picture taken wouldn't attract more tourists per year than this town now sees in an average century.

A welcome boost in tourist revenue from our current zilch.

You know it.

Don't lie.

So do they.

So why?

Why nothing? Why nought but a crap cartoon in a shady passage?

And that could be anyone with a beard.

Last time passed someone'd scratched 'penis' into it.

Why? Not why 'penis', why don't they make like pigs in shit?

Descending generations of denial. Begun in bad conscience, conscious at first, for a time, a generation of knowing nobs or two, but long sunk into reflex.

Some mill-owning Bounderby with the Corporation in his back-sack marching this very street am now hobbling, maybe heard some scruff laugh behind his back, thrashed a copy of Household Words out of his hide.

Or a local Gradgrind mocked by cheeky boys at the back of class.

Are there clues in the text long hidden to modern eyes which were once an unambiguous signpost, a banshee scream to the lofty denizens of this township?

Angry meets in the Corporation board room, tables thumped, spittle-flecked roars.

"This is us! That fucker is having a right dig!"

Deny everything lads, and deny it big.

Then on it rumbled, handed down. Alderman to Alderman, Mayor to Mayor, bastard to bastard, never explained nor articulated after that initial decision.

Unspoken, understood, until in time is civic instinct, and in this way,

Coketown is still denied and now the killing bullets ricochet.

Get all that down to three paragraphs, four tops, near the top, *then* it's a good start.

Citations needed.

Although not urgent that latter.

Shore up Wellington and find out whether those local troops were local troops by virtue of being billeted in this town's huge barracks or if they were a death squad from elsewhere despatched by the aristocracy and the word local is itself yet more manure.

Which of the other militarised milltowns were also army towns?

Was this town the head of the octopus, extending red-coated tentacles north, south, east and west from our fortress?

Acquire that information.

Source it. Reputably, sustainably.

Probably online somewhere.

Eventually.

Cautiously.

Don't pretend research isn't a can of worms you are reluctant to open. There are aspects of this story which, given passage of time and imperfect record, can never be known.

Easiest thing ever to sit down and read everything, every word, every witness account, every official document, every trace, every mark on the matter in every medium.

But what then? Do I then know what happened?

Even though I know full well the record is partial, and that I can't even begin to know what I don't know?

What if I confuse knowing all that can be known with actually knowing all that took place? Might I betray Socrates? Nobody knows nothing but people pretend they do every day non-stop, millions.

Look at the poisoned Russians. Nobody knows anything, then or now, but within a day halfwits were falling over themselves to declare war and get us all incinerated.

There were no dead ducks I know that.

What will be achieved by holing up in the library, hoisting dusty tome after dusty tome, investing hours, days, weeks, to make sure the Duke of Wellington was demonstrably a lethal foe of this town?

Of course he was.

Or weeks poring over documents piecing together an unanswerable case proving once and for all that this town was Coketown?

Of course it was.

And is.

The aim was never a meticulous accumulation of all available data placed in logical order then woven into a page-turning yarn.

If that's what you want jog on.

Can't help you.

Don't want to.

Probably against you.

You and your obsession.

Too great a depth of detail is a drowning pool.

Detritus to sink in while sharks circle unseen.

Fact-burdened process for the trivial-minded fool.

They'll be fingering fish-bones and bus tickets when the door comes in.

Not that I'm knocking them. Am probably jealous. Good luck if information is where they find meaning. Consolation in this indifferent cosmos remains the name of the game.

Get it where you can, even meaningless profusion.

Grease the wheels, ease the perpetual abrasion.

Who cares if it's all an illusion?

It's easy to laugh at the man who learns Klingon or gets cremated in a Star Wars suit.

That's why everyone does and so do I.

Never refuse a laugh, always throw your head back and bray.

Blissfully oblivious several seconds and no financial outlay.

Just laugh knowing your own beliefs and values and interests and loves are of no greater depth, are no less pathetic, than dressing-up as Darth Vader in late middle-age to visit an exhibition centre and pay silly money for 40 year old toys and picture-books.

Your family, your children, your job, your mortality.

None of it any more or less absurd than an accountant obsessed with Boba Fett.

Again, again, be honest at outset.

I can't be Antony Beevor! Ha ha, I wish!

To try is purest futility.

Lack temperament and basic ability.

A shame. Big hungry audience this.

A history-mad era, ours you know,

and war best way to go to strike dough.

Millions of men my age and thereabouts determined to know exactly how the wars went down before they perish, and fuck-all much else.

Men with thick books.

Thick books, thick necks.

Thick beards, more and more.

Beefies.

I've had these men explain battles to me in such incredible detail – numbers, decisive moments, strategic blunders, bold gambits, thrusts, heroes, villains – that I could have happily dashed out their brains with a rock.

Genealogy for ladies. Not sexist, just true. Look at the designs of the various magazines in WHSmith, they know their audience.

None of this can make the book. Why risk it? People these days. I'm not sexist.

Who Do You Think You Are?

Who Do You Hope To Be?

Why Do You Even Care?

What If You Are Nothing From Nowhere?

What If You Find Out The Family Tree Has Been Pissed On?

Snooty Auntie Rose decided to have a look see.

And in her dad's dad's dad found a big mystery.

Seems he'd rocked up on the lam from somewhere, nobody knows where, and the family name was almost certainly an alias, assumed to cheat justice.

Rose found a new hobby.

History can be our worst enemy.

Was ever a time so in thrall

yet unwilling to learn its lessons?

What if those who remember the past are condemned to repeat it too?

Which past, whose?

We each see through filters no less true,

to us, to them, to me, to you.

Which of the Chuckle Brothers went UKIP?

The dead one?

No, Christian fundamentalist.

No, that was Tommy Cannon.

Each an island unto ourselves, a sea all our own on a different plane, parallel but ever remote, remote as are the dead to matters of teen fashion.

Of course there is an objective past and one day robots free of our guiding hand might crowdfund and write it up.

But we never will.

Not in our nature or skill.

So this can't be that kind of book,
nor a stab to be at all.

Guestimate a small truth,
the suitably modest goal.

A few laughs and some doggerel.

What do we remember?

Why do we forget?

Would knowing change anything?

Will people wake up?

Woah, don't take the 'wake up' line.

Be saying 'sheeple' next to no time.

Finish the job, scrape 'CUNT' across your forehead with a bradawl.

If anyone were even there to be awoken it won't be by my scrawl.

Besides, those in the market for messiahs have long made their call.

Cleaving to Gods and monsters around the world tonight,
in connected digital isolation, psyched up for the fight.

Meanwhile more and more seek no saviour, having found one in themselves.

Massed individuals, communal lonely, unique doppelgangers, IKEA shelves.

You can always find what you're looking for in the depthless self, it has no bottom and the deeper you go the more intoxicating your suffocation.

You'll always find something in there as a consequence of looking, until one time you look and you don't, cue desperation.

Common development in middle-aged men.

One I knew, the summer just gone.

They found a note.

"Don't want to get old," he wrote.

And now he won't.

Stupid bastard, nobody does.

You're always younger than you'll ever be.

However old today, always older tomorrow

and when finally you ain't you never know.

Maybe down the road they'll freeze heads so a select few can watch the heat death of everything.

Maybe you're all babies on the first step of endless treks.

Science dangles new eternities, in lieu of those it wrecks.

The frightened finite leap to take the bait.

Touch the hem of a new priesthood, and wait.

Had a pint with him a few month before,

and do you know you couldn't tell?

Laughing, same as ever, and meanwhile in Hell.

He was already dead. We all are. But death I can live with if the book cops a half-decent review, makes me a few quid, and maybe helps me snag an advance for the next one.

The next one.

Write this one first.

Never make The Saracen's for seven now.

Should have cut through the park.

Full of nutters lately though.

And nights drawing in, not seven and dark.

Set forth tardy. Still time my comings and goings against a mental map drafted when I could open my legs and show my class, i.e. walk very fast.

Striding days over now, a mighty limp of late.

No more the strolling player, right hip in this state.

Swing the leg like a side of back bacon hung from the pelvis, subtle pitch left from shoulder to waist get the meat airborne, clench trunk on touchdown, ready and expecting lightning up the arse.

And yes, I have handled a side of back bacon. Many. And middle. And streaky. A short stint of butchery.

Enjoyed it. Keen knife play. You don't want to see how easy those knives part flesh.

Only the gelatinous bass oscillations of tripe in its uncut state, a huge juddering clod, wriggling alive in my arms, turned me away.

Bone memory of the vibrations with me to this day.

Curiously this swinging bacon limp is aesthetically similar to one I feigned in boyhood.

Mostly but not always as defensive strategy,

when crossing less familiar or hostile territory.

Those bits of town the wise traverse careful,

best skirt, never linger, danger.

Thinks: Who would twat a cripple?

Answer: Less people than would happily twat an able-bodied stranger.

Sound reasoning and nobody did twat a cripple, thank fuck.

At least not this bogus one. Hedged bets, rode my luck.

You'd have to ask the genuine handicapped brigade for a clearer picture of the risks,

but sure a few will have lucked out down the years and copped some licks 'n' kicks.

More now you'd expect, and worse, kindness having withered and died.

The culture changed for the handicapped, collective humanity was incrementally decried.

Okay we took the bad piss, but at least the State took good care.

Now you can't even use the word spacker to describe someone who ain't a spacker, but the State can deny a real spacker a suitable mobility chair.

Not that I use that language at all.

Disabled children alone tolerated, but age will push them into the firing line, prove you've got no legs once every two years you fucking scrounging swine.

People get tipped onto the pavement and beaten by patriots stirred with a burning sense of being cheated, robbed, swindled, by anyone and everyone, everyone except those who are actually cheating, robbing and swindling them.

Be some fine irony to catch a kicking now as a bonafide hopalong.

If still a betting man I'd have a tenner on the maze of red brick streets traversed from flat to main drag as the likely arena of punishment.

Rougher by the day, too near the station, slum terrace ravines of multiple-occupancy, kicked-in doors and trainers laced together over every second telephone wire.

Or maybe on the trailing end of the main drag itself, the foot of the hill I climb.

A long slow burn from river to railway, lined either side by bed and breakfasts housing feral men, some women, girls, boys, small children, so many small children too.

I saw some play barefoot in the snow, thin clothes, the little buggers were blue.

Saw a man smacked and his head shoved through a window of one last week.

Would have intervened but from the sound of their debate on my approach it was clear the recipient had somehow brought it upon himself, failing to uphold his end of some bargain or other.

So what can you do?

"Makin' a cunt of me y'fuckin' cunt?!?"

Bang, crash, scream, walk on by,

du-du-du-du-dooo, walk o-o-on by,

with my loaf and mince and onion pie.

My own beating will not be just, thoroughly the reverse.

Turn it over in my mind now and then, crucifixion fantasies perverse.

Mine shall be a masterpiece of loving cruelty, a whooping celebration of sadism and torment. An assault like those which confirmed it was time to get out of newspapers or swing my legs over a motorway bridge.

"Ha ha haaa, he's fuckin' shit his self!"

Blood pissing from both lips I feel hot shame swell my seat and try to rise from the spattered kerb. A contemporary training shoe with styling lost on me swings into view, puts my left retina in fragments, kills the eye, fractures the socket too.

A beating rich in the kind of detail I once cadged off the record off the cops off the back step of the cop shop, over a fag, after the official briefings, fishing for titbits.

Stuff which rarely made the paper. Judged too much for readers, too much in case some kiddy picks it up and is scarred for life.

Although everyone knows children never read newspapers today.

Although everyone knew the little beasts would lap it up anyway.

Kids today.

Shakes fist at sky. Homer's dad, pathetic, old and cold.

I've no kids and am riven by sorrow and bitterness.

By envy, that's the truth, isn't it?

The titbits got too much in the end.

Broken bottles jammed in places.

All the stamped on faces.

Made me scared and nostalgic.

But people *were* nicer once, even the bastards, and there *were* less of them.

That isn't some 50-year-old man's fantasy.

I'm not 50 until later this year.

In exactly two months.

But they were nicer. At least round here.

Certainly round the pubs.

Of course there was violence.

We're violent animals full of hate,

pleasure in pain a very human trait.

We're lucky every street isn't running blood and crunchy with teeth.

Take it from one who knows, who has hurt and been hurt, punched and been punched, kicked a man in the head, in the face, been kicked in the face and the head.

This chi is balanced che. Didn't really enjoy either, it must be said.

But less troubling now, in hindsight,

to have stopped a boot with my mouth,

than put a teethbound boot in flight.

Theoretically. On paper, where nobody lives.

Stone cold sober, giving. Saw and still see, heard and still hear, felt and still feel, each instant with clarity, no comforting fuzz, the bone and cartilage reverberation which yet echoes in physical memory like said tripe oscillation.

Burst my right Dr Marten, flung his head back,

saw him days later and half his face was black.

Be nice to say this atrocity cured me of thuggery.

Sadly can't, that came only from being beaten to buggery.

Besides. He was a cunt. Had it coming, personally owed.

Epiphany came six or so months later, on the deck of a 'do', writhing in the beer and docker broth of a working men's sprung dancefloor.

The light bulb pinged with that first kick in my head, blazed brighter when a blue suede Samba found my face, then illuminated each impact, gut, kidneys, bollocks, neck and one clean hard toe-bung *right* up the sphincter, having by then dived beneath a table, hanging onto the back legs, offering up my arse to protect a split and oozing head.

The educational tumult of pain and shock and fear,
obscured in memory, buried under several hours beer.
Only glimpses of twisting grunting within the legion swinging feet remain.
Camera flashes, gifs, Polaroids of my best friends and I under the boot.
A cathartic experience commended to all.
Makes you think, a drawn-out battering.
You learn something about yourself. You maybe start to think that maybe you'll die.
In any case an extreme example and far from indicative of the wider culture vis-à-vis violence of the rose-tinted era in question.
Civility still the norm. Generally they'd invite you to go, or you would them, they'd knock you down, or you would them, and that was that, the matter was at an end.
"Have you had enough?"
Genuinely asked or got asked.
The nastiness crept in. A routine precautionary kick became de rigueur in the 80s – specifically a kick not kickings – a kick to be sure. Put that down to soccer casuals bringing battlefield tactics into the nitespots, although am guessing, cherry-picking from a drink and drug saturated memory more hole than truth.
Might be making it up.
At worst, mass rolls aside, one-on-one, a solitary stiff shoe, just to be sure they're staying down. That's all mine was. More and more phet and uppers about by then, game boys, full of beans, be safe.
Only then offer the way out.
But stamping?
Never stamping. Never once they're sparked, never jumping in the air for impetus.
Or definitely less. I'm guessing again.
Making things up. I do that. I persuade myself.
People stamp each other a good deal lately,
share the clips on Twitter and Facebook.
You'll have seen the clips, had a fleeting look,
glimpsed a world you know little and fear greatly.
Some idiots blame hip-hop. Or violent video games. Or something something

something else, as and when their scapegoating is shown up as cock and balls. Not that it is wholly cock and balls.

Violent video games or any cultural product which places violence in a narrative context with the potential for guileful violence in and of itself to prevail will clearly make people that bit more open to the concept of using violence.

Monkey see monkey do, we ain't so smart.

Is total Christian myth to set us apart.

Simple levers, push and pull.

Nobody watched A Clockwork Orange for so long their legs congealed and they died. That's the difference now.

To hear some clowns culture exists in a separate realm, a sealed domain, enter as rational decision makers, coldly engage, then depart, the same.

Culture's true nature, true potency – as polymesmeric defining force for how we think and understand and shape ourselves, through which we identify and order emotions and impressions and establish what is and is not cool, particularly in adolescence, a state now extended to the grave, septuagenarian full-kit-wankers in baseball caps – is rejected.

Find studies that prove me wrong then stuff them up your arse. The future will prove me right, like William Blake. Accept you're a malleable potential thug ape or go and live in a church is the choice we make.

Sod the Saracen's for seven, sod even trying.

Nip down Clair Street.

Need get out from behind this couple any road. Trailed them since gaining the hill and they're hurting my head.

He a lanky skeleton, marl trackie, mid-20s maybe younger, hard-bitten, from his tone, demeanour, lexicon, walk, attitude. She a shapely blonde, a brassy lass of similar age, pushing a pram, all over the pavement, wonky wheels.

Lads like him up and down this hill, in and out the B&Bs. Local beat pig got one shut down. Proudest achievement in a long career, he told the paper, upon retirement, which he planned to spend on his narrowboat.

All the bodies rotting in there were sent elsewhere to impact on property prices and be tutted by twats like me.

And the girl's making me feel like a dirty old bastard, which I don't relish.

Swearing wanton mouth, clothing tight, skirt, short, revealing, provocative, alive in a way I am no longer. She'd kill me, fuck me juiceless, yet here I am,

gawping, lusting this fate.
Dirty old bastard.

"You should be fuckin' pushin' this you're stronger than me!"

'Pram's fucked, push one way wheels go the other way.'

"I know! I'm fuckin' pushing! You said you'd fuckin' get another!"

'I'll get another.'

"You said that fuckin' weeks back."

'I'll get another.'

"Will you stop looking at everyone like you want to twat 'em?"

'I do half of 'em. The bastards wanking over you I do.'

"They ain't wanking over me."

'They fuckin' are.'

Able to confirm every man and pubic boy coming down the hill has wanked over her, often turning, once by, to gorge their eyes, wank over receding pert arse, firm thighs.
She'll be 20, petite, slim, long hair, bleached. A Razzle dazzler. Of course they're wanking over her. And of course I'm wanking over her.
And nobody can be judged because everybody wanks.
Humanity will leave this universe on its knees, either praying or frigging, possibly both, count on it.
A relief to nip left at the bank not the wank-bank into empty Clair Street.
Down to the statue, draw strength from the three murdered men.
Finish this joint, up across the market to the Saracen's then.
Three who should be four, by the by.

Never occurred until recently but maybe three because one was from out of town.

Mr Lancaster of Blackburn.

Sounds off but you live and learn.

Funded by local TUC so more likely shy of dough.

That said this town fucking hates the Rovers though.

The three figures writhe and contort, faces twist.

One clutches his trunk, mouth an eternal 'oooooooo'.

You only get an oooooooo with a bullet in your belly.

The soldiers are one block. Four heads in peaked caps rise from merged bodies, merged as only uniforms and years being yelled at merge men.

Four barrels protrude, matt steel rods,

point straight as dies at the poor sods,

no ricochets in this representation.

This public art lacks balance Beryl.

Of course another big change is there was nowhere near same amount of coke around.

Hate fuel.

Stamping tackle.

Never saw coke, hardly ever.

Coke was rare and huge, for Bowie and the Rolling Stones, not your Smiths and Jones.

Not in this town. Now it's everywhere and nothing.

Nothing for me since a decade and more ago, the tasteful fitted kitchen of an accountant once known.

A four-eyed gimp, pure Poindexter, a good telly but dull as a sack of cement,

mate of a mate, haunted briefly to scope the odd satellite-only sporting event.

Was this a fight?

Think it was a fight.

And there's Penfold chopping to shame Belushi.

Exile On Suburban Street.

Not one thing that hole in the air does is worth doing too, twigged.

Never liked it any case.

Dabbled didn't linger, dipped a curious finger.

Never sufficiently minted to either get the taste or glibly erase the pleasing and costly effects of alcohol.

The Grandmaster knew.

I heard his message.

Expect you did too.

You were warned by a killer 45.

And now there's over-50s chasing midweek nights in the bogs of Sizzling Steak Pubs.

Always happiest to roll home dozy on dope and ale.

Peaceable if bawdy, a nodding bleary yeasty head,

a slash or spew worst sin en route to spinning bed.

A tossed kebab, a nicked glass smashed,

gardens in the nice streets trampled on Grand Nationals.

Piffle, trifles.

Now head uptown every third punter seems wired. Or am I just old and disturbed by the fierce kinetic energy of youth?

That I am now old cannot be denied – 49 is old, no matter what Sunday supplements say.

Imagine a salad sandwich that age. A mound of putrescence. A biohazard.

The police know the score. Armoured coppers, dog-vans, tasers, the whole works.

We never had that.

Nor widespread gak.

Or Red Bull and voddy.

Or steroids.

Big thick necks on the 'roid lads, and that's lots of the lads.

The waxy men, the swollen neo-Edwardian machismo, hair scraped hard across furrowed brows, patrician parting upstairs sculpted whiskers downstairs.

What do you see?

The last stand of a redundant archetype, acting out in the face of a future they fear but which doesn't really exist, the neutering female who will not rest until she turns all Alpha Males into beta cucks.

Some of 'em. Some just have weak chins and glom onto the style to mask facial inadequacies.

All the same, one day the obvious synergy between resurgent fascism and the rise of swollen neo-Edwardian machismo will strike people between the eyes.

Ours will be an era looked back upon with incredulity and contempt.

How couldn't they see?

What were they thinking?

How couldn't they see?

In our defence, smug future pricks,

we flail blind and wild in the midst.

Treading water, dark waves transfix us, powerful undercurrents pull and push tired legs, we're worn and destabilised.

Tomorrow, for you, we're fixed points to measure,

turn over our flaws in your mind, at your leisure,

a documentary series on 5 for your viewing pleasure.

Dead and gone, humans become comprehensible.

Just bear in mind people were scared.

Scared for themselves.

Scared for their kids.

But more for themselves and their consumer durables.

Scared of the cowardice they know they will display come marching day.

Remember that Saturday when the football lads who wanted little Tommy home in the bosom of his family met in the capital then waded into the ranks of massed bacon?

That was wake up time.

Changed the paradigm.

Until then been laugh out louds about a coming mobility scooter coup, UKIP gramps on the barricade, Sanatogen-bottle Molotov cocktails too, they'll burn the Reichstag after 9.30am! Once the bus pass kicks-in, see, so they can bring up their toothless reinforcements for free.

But laughter came hard, choked in the throat, watching Dibble chased up the road, ducking stiff-arm shoves and hurtled cans, driven back by nutters up for anything, no fucks given.

Every Guardian liberal on a mighty march for this or that or the other in a carnival atmosphere feat. innovative street art and a competition for the best snarky placard is great, a lovely sight.

Ottolenghi's protest picnic tips.

But 10,000 of these headcases would slice through like bricks cleave water.

Don't get me wrong, they'd end up twatted – the myth of the weedy effeminate leftist man is a far right homoerotic fantasy – weight of numbers would tell.

But no bother, to them, was the message.

They're up for a street scrap, heavy stuff, trading with a gobful of smashed teeth and blood gashing out their sore pink face.

Don't worry too much.

They won't win.

Unless they do.

Placards won't stop them, that's for true.

Gentle wit won't beat them back. Sooner or later someone will have to stop them, smash them, fists and boots, be ready to stop boots and fists in the doing.

But who?

And what will YOU do if nobody does and they do win?

History tells us 'how do I best keep my head down' will be Radio 4's thought for the day.

Fall in behind the strongman like the Brazilian middle classes.

Expect lots of the centre to cross the floor before pain comes to their door.

I can't take chances with the family, I work hard. My first obligation is to them, and you know what, there *are* a lot of scroungers, and if they aren't working why *are* they here? And Christ!

Women have forgot their place.

Trees that cannot bend snap in the storm.

Dickens' Stephen Blackpool couldn't bend and so snapped.

Anyway, whatever comes next my hip has surely bagsied me a spectator's seat.

I'd be no use in a running battle, a war on the street.

Leggy fucking Mountbatten?

Where do we get our sicknotes validated?

Ha ha, if only.

We're all in this together.

All in line for fists and leather.

2

Odd to think, as simple motion of ball in socket pops bright pain squibs and the promise of potential rockets into my pelvis then on around the skeleton, that once I limped for fun.

Not that prudent camouflage hobble, purely for the crack.

Limping not against anticipated duress, in the name of play.

A pantomime affliction of upper right thigh stroke back,

dragging the same appendage which blights my gait today.

Déjà vu-doo?

Limped bored around shopping centres and precincts, concrete plazas.

Awkward, wincing, my wince could break your heart, that dismay only fleeting betrayed, and gulped down, *the little stoic*, grimly I'd smile through the non-pain, warranted frown turned defiantly upside down.

Worse things to do in childhood than affect and discard impediments for either entertainment or safety. Knew kids who killed cats.

And trust me it is a future tell, they're all still fucked.

Reminds a boy how lucky he is to have his health.

Walk a mile in another man's corrective shoes...

Or a lap of the precinct, the precinct just by the Saracen's, more than once.

My limping boy presented a happy shining face,

and I think made the world a better place.

How many passers-by left pondering the triumph of hope over tragedy represented in this doughty child, battling the hand fate dealt, a beacon of youthful positivity?

Visible shows of concern moved me.

As such showings still do,

although in number now few.

Old men are meant to limp, it draws no response.

Which came first, limping as sport or as insurance?

Chicken, egg, if ever known is now lost. Maybe one day I'll bite into a mint Viscount and all will come flooding back, but until then your guess is as good as mine.

Speculating, knowing my ways, tainted by my prejudices about how people are, watchful gleaning beasts, am inclined to suspect strategy arose from fiction.

Sorrow and pity, glimpsed at play,

ape brain twigs be useful one day,

and so it is duly filed away.

Which then begs the question of cause.

Why might a nimble child – Springheeled Jack at that age, a writhing eel on the line, a flare-clad faun – begin limping in the first place?

This I know. Overheated imagination meet culture.

Specifically telly. Raised by the box.

Specifically films. Specifically the old war films.

Obsessed.

Saw all the old war films. Played all the old war films. Wasteland behind the street, me, our kid, all the lads from around, diving behind bushes, mouths making machine-guns.

Lived all the old war films.

Always a limper sooner or later in the old war films, usually the cool defiant one. The grunt with the begrudging salute.

Slug in the leg? Undaunted. Bite down, plough on, have a cig, limp, fight, kill, limp, smoke, limp, soldier on, foil-pack, leave me, save yourselves, a last stand, a last fag, limp and smoke to victory or glorious death.

Obviously am a smoker too.

Wall-to-wall that war back then. Never the first war, always the second.

Toys and games were that war, comics were that war, half the TV shows were that war, afternoon matinees were that war.

There was a massive u-boat on the sideboard throughout childhood, a plastic sea wolf looming over the ornaments, the ersatz Capo Di Monte rose and brass Basset hound, jubilee mug and Shire horse.

Sections cut away to betray inner workings and pea-sized sub-aqua Nazis scurrying the exposed passages.

The u-boat not the Shire horse.

Pride of place until it fell apart from being ragged by me.

The u-boat not the Shire horse.

Our kid was Airfix mad, countless were, and little did more to keep the war physically alive in the British psyche than these accurate scale renderings of the

I awoke with a B-29 Superfortress turningout of a bombing run four feet above my face.

engines of that war.

For the ten years we shared a bedroom I awoke with a B-29 Superfortress turning out of a bombing run four feet above my face.

How many Spitfires and Hurricanes and ME109 and Heinkel He 111 frozen mid-dogfight over how many boys in their beds, half-awake and dreaming, confused and masturbating?

Airfix stormtroopers posed a carpet treading risk to rival LEGO. Every home had the lad flinging a stick-grenade lurking in a mat, poised to blitzkrieg sensitive stockinged insteps.

Limping to victory.

Now limping to the pub.

The doctor suggested a stick.

I joked, 'What's brown and sticky?'

"Shit," he said.

'Not yet,' I said.

Final piece of the jigsaw.

Coming soon, all one need know.

Go easy. Rest when can. Anticipate decline, rapid perhaps.

Gone for good, fucked for keeps.

As have sown so now reaps.

Because self-inflicted, same as most grief for everyone, being honest.

Inflicted through the way I found to console myself.

The way I used to run this town.

Run this town every day, every which way you can imagine,

in the avenues and alleyways, where the soul of a man is easy to buy.

Early, always, while you boggled in your pit, locating then scratching your arse, remembering who you are, the things you do, whether you are happy or suicidal.

The Saracen's. Shithole. Why are we here?

Douglas Bader.

SS Action Man.

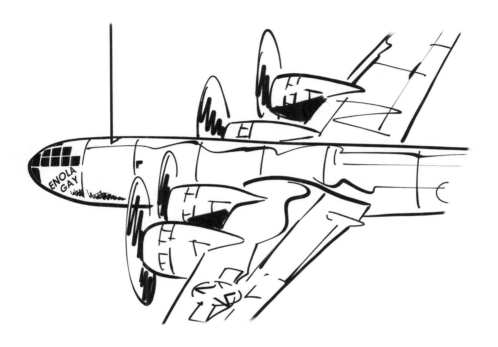

3

'The fucking Saracen's?'

"Yeah."

'It's a shithole!'

"I ain't been in 20 year."

'No fucker has, it's a shithole.'

"We've never met there have we?"

'Only time *ever* went there was on off chance of cheap fags and that out the bag.'

"That's what I said."

'Last time I went in there it was me and a dozen skinheads and a pit-bull on the threshold.'

"Hardly get up that end since we moved here."

'Snarling, I thought it was going to have my bollocks off.'

"I heard years ago it got shut down."

'It did, after that riot, but a new bloke come in. Why'd he say the fuckin' Saracen's?'

"That's just where he said."

'What did you say?'

"When."

'When he said let's meet at the fucking Saracen's.'

"No, I said when'd he want to meet. Saturday at 7."

'Even better, all the worst cunts off the match two hour and ten pint into it.'

"I might be a bit after 7, I'm picking the boys up from football."

'They'd better fuckin' win. What's his number now?'

"Same."

'Same as what? I ain't got the fucker's number.'

Monday that, Nye down the line.
Lads' reunion, first in some time. Be Christmas the last.
Tommo got in touch set it up,
in touch with Nye not I. Out the blue.
Tommo vanished from the face of this town,
and the Earth far as anyone knew.
Faded out to be precise. Didn't go with a pop more a pft.
Ebbed from view over a decade or two until it was an annual Christmas pint at best, then seldom even that, then flit.
Got told of a venture he'd started,
dodgy as the day is short, their word,
whatever, he took the piss then sharted,
ran-up debts and enemies they'd heard.
Be five year ago cut and ran. Someone said he was on Facebook a while but what cunt looks at that?
Now home for a visit and summoning the first pint of the old lot in fuck knows how long.
Wonder if his sister's dead?
A meet had been mooted few months back but location and dates were

disputed until it peetered out.

Fewer and further between, these soothing nights of warm nostalgia, of spreading guts compared, mocking our own crumpling faces, sneering at bald spots and recent major health scare highlights.

Happily prodding the scars of time's ever closer shave in our bubble of shared fate.

Six or seven usually make the effort.

A tight mob we are, still. There is love.

None of us ever fucked none of the others over, over birds, cash, anything,

so never the splits and feuds and camps such shit must inevitably bring.

We'll laugh, drink, smoke, ask after those absent, remember the one that's absent for good, then off, promising to keep better in touch, get out more, a gig, book a narrowboat, then not doing any of those things.

Which suits everyone fine.

Life isn't Friends off the telly.

Less has to be more.

Healthy and natural to live in each other's pockets when finding your way in the world.

But then life, if you're lucky, makes change, and eventually I can't do any weekend between August and October.

Chance makes friends, change carries them away.

Time + distance x obligations = "If we meet in Manchester it'll take me three hours to get home so the last train I can catch is at 7pm and fuck that."

See Nye fairly regular, one or two others similar.

Proximity and viable public transport keeps friendship rolling,

buses and trains crucial, we don't meet for ten-pin bowling.

Not always geographical though. Tommo began the process of vanishing the day he got hitched. Still in the same house, didn't move away, just stopped leaving it. Happens. I've got me hole now, why go out? Houses are man-made caves for apes.

Doubt he's been seen a dozen times since. Last for me ASDA car park one Christmas, 2012 or around, in a flash motor mashing his horn trying to run me over.

We can't have had more than two or three proper drinks together since his stag-do.

Proper stag-do. Old haunts on the eve of the wedding not a two grand weekend in Bruges 18 month before the nuptials.

Started well, groom scuffling with a wino he tried make look a prick for no reason.

Sunny city street Saturday noon, rammed Yates terrace.

High, laughing, pavement thronging, along comes this tramp.

Familiar face since childhood, fixture of the town centre, total wreckhead but nice bloke, and savvy if you caught him sober.

Always after a fag, never money just a fag.

Knocking on by then, silver hair and shrivelled.

Two sons on the street, neither sharp as dad.

Once gave one son a black pork pie hat, stolen.

He sported it proudly round town for a stint then next time seen he's hatless and battered, scuffed and burst purple face swollen.

Brother'd twatted him for the hat.

Charity eh?

Tommo shouts something so hilarious at this tramp I've totally forgot it and next thing he's over the wrought iron fence coming straight at Tommo, tables, chairs, drinks going over, and there's about three blokes struggling to hold him back, and he's pointing straight at Tommo screaming "*YOU* are a *CUNT!*" again and again, just that one line, same intonation every time, forever it felt.

Beautiful. Powerless. What can you do? You can't leather a little old dosser at noon on a busy High Street, nor can you reason with him.

You just have to absorb. We laughed ourselves sick then got bored and so did he and we gave him loads of fags and off he fucked.

They're all dead now, him and his sons. Last one froze in the doorway of BHS.

Called the number Nye gave. Tommo never picked up.

Texted, no reply.

Now here we are. Head of the market, opposite the glowing frosted glass eyes of the Saracen's Head.

Worst pub in this town bar none.

Well, that's not true.

Know four or five out the edge, get dropped second they knew no fucker in there knew you.

But worst in the centre, full stop. Rough as you like, always, crap ale and scrap-hunters, always, and all it'll ever be.

Pubs seldom change for the better. Bad pubs hardly ever come good. Good pubs more prone to go bad. And when good pubs go bad they hardly ever come good again.

Can't think of one.

Castle maybe.

Castle.

Not the definite article.

Neither on sign nor wall.

Just Castle.

Castle *half* decent again. Half. Darker, again, at least.

Everywhere you looked there was a bulb in your eyes.

Unwind under Gestapo interrogation.

Dream pub when Grace ran the operation.

One of those where nights began and often ended, events permitting, or even stayed put, weather depending, if a good crowd in. Good music. Bouncing nights.

Nowhere near that now.

Better, but not there. All lost when one prick got his name over the door.

That's all it takes.

Grace died, Bill took her place.

Miserable bald droopy 'tache-faced fat shortarse.

We didn't get on.

No sooner installed than 'closing for refurbishment',

a sentence which is a death sentence 99 times out of ten.

This new broom was a lethal injection. The gas in the chamber.

Chased us out of amber wombs, welcomed us back to sepia cheesemakers.

Old photos of men and truckles, not even taken round here. Random retro dairymen from the warehouse of generic pub shit for urban publicans feeling rustic.

Bill screwed tools to the walls.

Fastened a hoe over the jukebox.

Red velvet and copper purged for chintz and pine and lights, so many lights, spots, lamps, a lamp trained on every picture of cheese and cheesemen, a ring of candle bulbs on a cartwheel in the saloon.

All the warmth of an industrial laboratory.

Lot of pubs went that way back then.

Screwed rakes next to dartboards, piled in illumination.

Wanted more women over the step, they found the darkness forbidding.

Probably needed doing, I think,

Stone Age, the then politics of drink.

Met a lass in Castle one Friday night summer 1989,

her with a half-a-dozen mates, me and all of mine.

Clicked, fixed to head uptown next night the two of us.

Meet Castle 7.30 have a few then hop on a bus.

I'm bang on time Old Spice balls tingling, she's loitering on the step.

'Why didn't you go in?'

She put me straight.

Fat chance she'd go in a boozer alone, a bar uptown maybe but not this joint, young lass like her, order a drink and wait, read the paper, have a fag, throw a dart or two.

Wives and girlfriends welcome, groups tolerated, single women? *We'll stare at you.*

Maybe that was just the North. Towns like this.

You hear horror stories about parts of Yorkshire.

Post-refurb Castle was like being inside a large crate. Bare wood floor wood ceiling wood panelled halfway up the walls.

Slate tiles round the horseshoe, smash every glass dropped, as happens every night at every busy bar, pissed punters picking up more slippery vessels than they could carry stone cold sober let alone howling shitfaced, then bumping about like dodgems.

The 10p jukebox of vinyl gold was gone. In its place a CD half-a-quid-a-pop bastard with more Queen and Meatloaf than anyone knew existed.

There's days of it. Days. Never bought the Queen reinvention. Shit men's rock.

Bubble burst one Friday to Meatloaf's Paradise By the Dashboard Light.

Autoplay warbles to an half-empty room of flowery settees,

a handful of bodies having a flyer then taking flight.

The air seething with flies, as it had been since re-opening night.

Not those tiny flies so slow they are impossible to seize.

Not beer flies.

Which are fruit flies by the way.

A certain aromatic gene in beer's activated yeast drives them bats.

Acts on the fruit fly like the scent of corrupt plums or rank kumquats.

I haunted dank digs by the wholesale fruit market for a time – a houseful of Finns and a Tyke bouncer who stabbed himself three times in the stomach for a compo scam, as we only learned from the pigs who came knocking after his moonlit flit – and drank in the pub by the main gate this while.

Never closed, foddering and pishing market workers and drivers and buyers betwixt and between their unsociable shifts.

Egg and chips and bread and butter, two slice, £1.50 round the clock.

Alive with weaving beer flies.

Fruit flies.

Humped on the market odd days, cash in hand. Bags of rot about, and fruit uneaten is a waiting womb.

A pallet of long gone lemons, thousands, to go in the bin.

And you could see the flies move beneath the liquefying skin.

Grey dots, ascending to – pop pop pop – shiny blackness on the surface.

Quick shake of the wings then away to cut mazy arcs around the tap room.

First port of call The Market Arms.

And not a million miles from there.

Castle got its share.

But this was not they. These were big fat hairy fuckers.

Juicy buzzers.

The gutting of this old building exposed a parcel of Victorian fly-eggs embedded in horsehair plaster, filthy with anthrax and worse, a buried curse, that was one theory going around.

The theory I made up and set going around.

The brood sprang into life soon as the fixtures and fittings were in and the heating went back on, once hot water coursed in the walls, coddling the swarm.

Insects every surface, each cubic yard of air,

on the landlord's pink dome as he pulls off an ale.

Drowning in the drinks to fish and flick wholesale.

'That pint'll have cholera in it now mate, you want to take that back.'

Dead ringer for another one bites the dust.

The Saracen's Head is not dead but half its customers half are.

These were big fat hairy fuckers. Juicy buzzers.

4

Fair crowd in, 25 or 30, feels more in this low-ceiling L-shaped room, and what with half of them being gigantic.

Meatballs. Ballheads. Many gleaming wet-shaved skulls. I'm Number One back and sides and feel like a hippy. Few look fresh off the match, scarves, jumping about.

Animated men. Not keen on the company of animated men, least of all big men, flapping their brawny limbs.

Everyone stand still, better still, sit the fuck down.

The music is so low can't place it but can hear enough to be relieved it is subdued.

Don't like or understand contemporary pop music, but that's how it's meant to be at 50.

Muffled suits.

Prominent memory of the odd pints here waiting for a gander in the holdall of goodies is 2Unlimited or similar educationally subnormal beats rattling fillings.

Where do you come from, where do you go, where do you come from, Cotton Eye Joe? Bum-ch-bum-ch-bum-ch-bum-ch-bum-ch-bum-ch-

And one or other window freshly burst, generally from the inside out, boarded over.

Closed a few times, been closed by police at least once. Fighting, drugs, stolen goods, a mass brawl brought the shutters down last time. An orgy of glassings, a stabbing, some cunt lost an eye and was lucky not to die.

Spilled onto pavement, raged until massed pork descended swinging truncheon meat.

Not long after I'd started on the paper. Eye-boy hovered on the brink a stint so they went to town, painted him up as an angel, schoolboy portrait in lozenge frame, mum's bedside vigil, even though we knew he was a cunt.

Location the Saracen's curse. Location and immediate built environment.

Arse-end of the centre for one.

Step off the front step, turn right then right again then left, 30 seconds to the ring road and gaze on a mill terrace labyrinth stretching far as can be seen.

A mostly potless maze of streets, tight 'n' tiny two-up-two-downs most, a Victorian red brick wedge flanked on two sides by its crumbling 20th century equivalents.

A swathe of bleak conurbation home to more streets where the wary are advised to limp than any other part of this town.

Home to this town's Eastern European arrivals and so good deli, nice one, and the longstanding Asian ghetto, if we may use the word ghetto to describe a British ghetto.

We tend not to, shame or cowardice? I don't know.

Maybe it was all a coincidence. Whoops-a-ghetto.

Know those streets well.

Our kid's in those streets.

I rented there, scored in the backs.

Scruffy mostly friendly, by day,

but nights of murder in the cul-de-sacs.

Business-related, but machetes all the same.

Stick to main drags after dark.

Well-lit pavement, avoid the park.

Be seen, be safe.

Limp like someone is watching.

Ran there often for the pure pleasure of twisting and turning.

Once, years ago, a swirling black and white sleet winter morning, I saw something.

Five miles or so into a run, breathing rhythmically, heart a scalding metronome, soaked through, extremities numb, everything else pain, mind gone, turned sharp right opposite the old infirmary to chase up toward the stadium –

And there, glimmering dully through the cold vortex, was the vast snake.

And I was on the snake, chasing up its back, over scale-cobbles showing silver in the wet light, curving alongside disused railway line on the left, to the distant brow, a wall of red homes, black windows, on my right.

Returned many times since, when conditions seemed auspicious, to see once more.

Never did. Now never will. Fucked hip knocked that on the head for sure.

Churlish now to complain,
all my own work, nurtured pain.
Felt it build gradually
did nothing, naturally.
We don't, men, if things are okay in the now. My maternal grandfather who I loved with all of my heart ignored the symptoms of untreated diabetes right up until the day he abruptly collapsed with it was rushed into hospital and shortly thereafter died.
Aches begat pain, pain begat agony, agony begat one ibuprofen, two, three, three and an aspirin, three and two aspirin, three and three aspirin, press on, ram through, tapped into some codeine, good stuff, available on 'script only, hillbilly smack, back to one pill, yes!
But then two, then three, three and an ibuprofen, then run out of codeine, so back to over-the-counter, dropping so many rattling like maracas.
Remorseless warding off.
Until a cool dawn,
Spring just gone,
a scream at the end of the street
as running right foot lightly touched tarmac.
Lung flattening, the kind of howl you hear inside your head for days, that rends your throat, with which you scare yourself.
Flames leap from arsehole, fireworks fill head,
grazed heap on pavement, leg functionally dead,
nothing, meat, drag it home for a fortnight in bed...
The Saracen's wide twin windows face the covered market, although eyes long closed, evaporated, atoms, will there have gazed upon an open market ground barely changed in the previous eight centuries.
The listed wood and iron canopy went up 50 years after the Saracen's opened, 1890-something. Rains a lot this town, it's why we got cotton. So they spent the best part of a millennia getting piss-wrapped before a roof crossed their minds.
Beersellers turned shilling round the market throughout. Haul your wares from hill to town, flog as best can, hit the grog, give change to wife, right back to Domesday.
More speculation. More guesswork. But one needn't know that is just how

it was to say that is just how it was. Deductive reasoning. Helped the Greeks discover atoms and humanity achieve many great feats.

A handful of humanity. The balance did sweet fuck-all. Ours is only in isolated instances a sophisticated species.

Don't let the technology in your pocket seduce you into thinking otherwise, you're ballast. Most are. In any case we have invented nothing. Everything evolved.

Computers arose like rabbits or fungus.

An inevitability from the second some ape noticed that logs roll and round ones roll best. And if I cut a slice across the width –

Apple comes from trees.

Wiping our arse rather than licking it clean about all that elevates us above animals.

That and music. Our beautiful music.

Although animal music can be beautiful too.

Well, birds' music.

Well, some birds' music.

Nothing beautiful ever came from the mouth of a goose.

Only – thinking about it this statement is lies.

By the river, dead autumn mist and muted sunrise,

a triangle of geese crosses low, bound for the estuary,

the sea, then on, bit of warm, the annual fuckee offski.

And their mournful hooting, rising then falling from distance to distance.

Will touch you.

Mammal music generally poo.

Anxious types play whale to get well.

But music of cats a soundtrack to hell.

Woke some nights back small hours to hear

a baby being waterboarded loud and clear.

Out the window I look,

fat tom by the hedge,

sqwarling for a fuck.

Caught a can on the windpipe instead.

A dozen-odd pubs had clustered about the market by the 1800s, a dozen-odd plus one when the Saracen's opened its doors somewhere in the middle.

But even then that spot was the arse-end.

Nothing at its back but the labyrinth, near-distant belching stacks, the dirty old coach then bus depot, the nick. Which brings us to the immediate bureaucratic environment which acted on the Saracen's as a potter's fingers on spinning clay.

The pub sits at the apex of a criminal Piccadilly Circus.

Back on the step, glance left, 20 yards, this town's first cop-shop.

Stroll 20 yards on from that, the old courts, crown and magistrates.

The pigs flew first, 1980s, all of 50 yards in the opposite direction. The courts followed suit, same heading, new complex approximate same distance as old.

The old Job Centre next door, the old dole next along after that.

They too moved. They too remain a minute or two distant.

This is the passing traffic from which the Saracen's core custom has been drawn.

Not that I'm knocking these ranks.

Everyone needs a place to go,

where everybody knows your name.

But mine ain't the Saracen's, thanks.

Yet here I am, to meet this mate unseen in Christ knows how long, and however long that is more again since last drank in this dive.

And there is Tommo, Noel Edmonds flashing at his back.

5

The book must be 30,000 words minimum.

Bare.

Not that literature is a numbers game.

But in the same breath of course it is.

Everything is.

That last book far too slight at the price.

Fourteen quid for a puffed-up novella?

And what are these? Poems?

Half these don't rhyme.

You're having a laugh mate.

Many need the reassurance of a thicker book.

Thickheads, but they're the ones I'm after.

Longer term they spend more freely on merchandise,

a few live ones might earn me a week somewhere nice.

But they expect some bang for their book buck.

Meet their heft test with a greater weight of words.

And I have made a good start.

A passionate introduction, not perfect, in need of correction.

First thing tomorrow, maybe later, illusory drunken inspiration.

Safe in the machine.

No.

Find memory stick, back up from the off this time. Lost the last, my first, half a book, machine died, never happened. Different person second time of writing. So memory stick or ballache.

Lead off on Dickens, chapter uno, in on the book, this town is Coketown, work back to the massacre, forward to the ricochet.

Maybe Dickens came in here, came in the Saracen's. Why wouldn't he visit the market's newest pub? Makes sense.

Wingback by the fire, hot punch, scratching notes.

Drawing deep on a cup of the steaming spiced brew, Charles noticed a quiet man with a gentle careworn face, huddled over small beer, warming himself inside and out near that same hearth.

Stephen?

That kind of thing, purple but not twirly. And he'd have welcomed a warm on his way around that January. A harsh winter from what can be gathered.

Or has been gathered.

Harsh in the Crimea, according to the Royal Collection Trust website.

You know, *the Royal Collection Trust website.*

Also cholera, although that again the Crimea. Not here, although there had been an outbreak in this town a few years previously.

Facts. Maybe it will be Stalingrad after all. Joking, it won't.

To reiterate, I am not Antony Beevor, and not through choice. Jude Law will never star in a bad blockbuster of my book so I'll have to live on sales.

Meaning privation.

Ah well I had a good run.

And how long do you want?

Or think you deserve to get?

Don't answer those questions.

First betrays your cowardice.

The second your delusions.

If Dickens walked in here right now he wouldn't hang about.

Edmonds flickering at his shoulder.

6

Table by the bandit, eight seats, seven empty, a solitary skinhead, nose in the barrel of an half-supped Stella, Adam's apple pumping, Edmonds flickering at his shoulder.

One of my very oldest friends.

And in truth a bit of a wanker.

But fundamentally sound.

Tommo not Noel.

Unless he has changed in personality as profoundly as he has in physique.

Tommo not Noel.

If not now, in truth, a bit of a fat wanker.

Which is unnecessarily harsh.

We are mates after all, albeit, as discussed, not through choice.

Cards dealt, circumstance,

played blind, pure chance.

When kids meet it's blank slates bumping together.

If we met stone cold the first time tomorrow,

two old filled-in men, we'd detest one another.

But pointless to nurse ill will over that,

to let it interfere with our friendship.

A friendship of four decades, first 20 spent binding ourselves tightly together unto the bitter end via the medium of profound shared experience.

Meaningful experience, things you aren't the same the other side of.

First fags

first drinks

first shags

not together

but tawdry shared in detail soon after

first spliffs

first trips

first scraps

first beatings

first whiteys

first near death experience in the front seat of his motor, four in the back, four wheels off the ground, revolving laterally along trees, at night, pitch blackness between the boughs, was a deer watching? Frozen mortified until wheels descended, tyres somehow bit.

And we sat on the verge in silence for a long time then rolled slowly back to town.

All treasures gathered when knees are springy and ballbags are tight.

Glimpsed through murk at present but awaiting our return in senility's clarifying light.

Met this hundred year old man. Met lots, local news fodder until people stopped dying, but this one was special.

What is your secret is the first question you ask, and they mutter something about single shots of whisky or fried breakfasts, this is the usual run of things.

But this man talked me unbidden through a football match in which he played, I assume, or perhaps watched, or dreamed. But in terms and detail so fine it was though he were seeing and living the game in real time on some other plane to that upon which we spoke.

I left him lifting the cup.

God grant us all the privilege of insensibility on the cusp of nothingness.

Politics would get in the way

if Tommo and I met today.

He'd take me for a Trot,

though I'm definitely not,

and I'd know he's a racist.

Because he plainly fucking is.

Or was getting that way, gradually becoming, last few times of asking.

Not a fascist or Nazi, must stress, strictly non-doctrinal malevolence.

No code or theory or wider worldview informed the sentiments.

Never couched in political terms, more a reflex rejection of everything not Tommo.

We, his friends, were presumably judged enough like Tommo to get a pass.

What I'm saying is he wasn't goosestepping around the youth club disco.

He was a good laugh. A maniac and petty criminal, but a benign git.

To us, at any rate, who grew to manhood coping with all his shit.

To everyone else slightly more of a menace.

And be sure he'd be that to me too were we meeting anew tonight.

Swinging at us after six pint, rough guess,

but missing, am good nick next that flab mess.

You're a big man but you're out of shape Alf Roberts.

Unless my hip give out then size would tell and he'd leather me.

Don't think it'll come to that.

We are mates, all said and done.

Mates from the streets and parks via desks and youth club pool table, football pitch to bus shelter and low level criminality, boys to men, coming of age, arm-in-arm, wreaking our slice of havoc. Initiating, enabling, sharing, and that's you, connected for keeps.

At a fundamental level you can't deny but will come to interrogate, perhaps strive to break, when they turn out to be a middle-aged wanker.

A wanker like Tommo. And I say that 100% confident he would or has or will or is at this second, under his breath or at the back of his mind, returning the compliment.

We're both of us right.

Still, he's my mate.

And my mate has dragged me to a shithole.

Can't be more than a yard of hair

on every head put together in here,

although only blokes and lads being fair.

Or –

Could that be a wife in the corner?

Half the crowd those sparse wastrels where every loose bone and wire in their skull is seen to move upon swig or drag. Few tubby steak pudding heads, few 'roid brick shithouses so fresh off the prison weights their veins are still up. Craniums shorn down to the wood clumped at the bar. If it wasn't for tats and piercings glinting you could take it for a dirty ball-pit. They –

What the fuck has happened to his face?

'Tommo! What the fuck has happened to your face?'

"Barney y'cunt! Long time, how's it hanging?"

'Straight down, banging my knee, what the fuck has happened to your face?'

Still trying to crush your hand like a Tory.
The light is dim but up close his face is a busy mix of shadows and bumps, not long faded, which tell the tale of a sound pummelling two or so month ago.
Maybe more, you heal slower as you get older until then you don't heal at all and damage lays upon you.

"I'll tell you, I'll tell you, what you having? Stella?"

'I'll get these.'

"Get us Stella."

'Nye not here?'

"Yeah, he's under the table sucking us off."

'Always had a way with animals that lad.'

What do I want to drink?
What is there?
Stella, Strongbow, Guinness, Carling Black Label, John Smith.
Spoilt for choice.
We have been spoiled. Last pint uptown was that new real ale place behind the town hall.
Beer from every corner of the world capable of squeezing out a drop.
Blackboard up with all the details, *menus*, map reference of farm which grew the hop,
and exactly where the farmer had a shit if caught short on his tractor.
All vital information for the CAMRA twat about town.
Not bad that said, lovely beer,
but fuck me, how dear?
As fuck, and being honest, bollocks.
20p off a fiver a pint in this town?

That's solely to keep the riff-raff out.

Although fuck me ain't short of riff-raff. But good luck to the lot.

Those setting such tariffs think you're riff-raff too, like it or not.

Paid four for a pint in one thought not bad, only it wasn't a pint it was a *schooner*.

I'm going, 'What the fuck is a schooner?'

Whiskers behind the bar explains is a measure they do for *enthusiasts* who want to taste lots of different beers in the course of a session.

Adds that the blackboard, if I had cared to read it, was quite specific about all of this.

Spate of these joints now. The spreading university props up a small hipster economy, night-time mostly, and the distant leafy suburbs, further flung market towns and villages, send their ruddy Mumford & Sons & Daughters into this ring.

And I don't mind 'em.

I don't mind hipsters.

I don't mind real ale twats.

Find them no bother. A little earnest at worst,

and worse things to be than earnest, if few so tedious.

No beef here with the middle class,

Tories aside, who can get fucking bent,

their pubs are alright for the older gent.

Put it this way, count yourself unlucky if you ever get a pot rammed up your chin in a pub where the scratchings are homemade and the landlord looks like Jesus.

Is places like the Saracen's you get spindles in your eyes.

'Stella and a Guinness mate.'

"Guinness is off."

That is the fucking nightmare right there.

'John Smi- Stella, two Stella.'

Life's too short for John Smith. Thank fuck.

Firm bump on my right shoulder.

"Sorry son."

Another bump.

Man next us at the bar trying pull his coat on but missing the sleeve. Fully extending his left arm every time to bop me lightly, push himself sideways slightly.

He sways and stinks of rich warm soil.

Peat.

Love a scotch but the stink of it on others turns my sober innards. Cloying.

Another bump.

"Sorry abou' tha' son."

Glaswegian.

Short, wiry, a brutally-lived 50 or hard-lived 60, impossible to say.

A pinched face, tight shrivelling, right eye bugged wallward, left eye a slit, eyes black like his hair and goatee, pierced apertures, flaps and prominences.

Lot of Scots this town. Always, more than the English average Corby aside my bet.

Railway. Main stop on the London-Scotland mainline since 1863 which is forever on a human scale.

Either this town as far as they could afford to get or got pissed en route and slung off.

I don't know. They're here, I know that, and I don't mind. Why would I?

"Seven-forty mate."

'Cheers, drop change in your –'

Bump.

"Ech, sorry son – here."

Grabs us round the back of the neck, tender but firm, pulls me in close to his grooved puss, and mutters smiling into my eye.

"I'm hookin' you son, bang bang, boxin' trainin' boxin' trainin'!"

He lets me go and we both laugh,
but only his laughter is genuine.

I'm hookin' you son.

7

'Cheers.'

"Cheers."

'Fuck all on that bar. Guinness is off and I hate Stella.'

"Don't mind it me."

'I blow up here.'

Prod the belly which fills with gas after five or six. I burp acid for days.

'What in fuck happened to your face then?'

"I'll tell you. You still at the paper then?"

'Took a cheque. Ready to kill someone, probably me'self. Where are you at now?'

"Back, here, near here. Since May."

'Should've give Nye a bell had a pint before.'

Although glad you didn't. Or am I? Wouldn't be here now. Bloody wish you had.
This homecoming would be over and done and I'd be on my sofa skinning up
and drinking tea, trying to fix my introduction.
More Dickens from outset.

"Few people I still needed not to see."

'That what happened to your face is it?'

"No, no, got them all boxed-off."

'Dead?'

"Paid 'em back."

'That usually works an' all. How's Shelley?'

"Fucked if I know."

'Sad to hear that.'

"I wasn't but she got the house and then I was."

'Are her and the kid round here?'

"Nah, stopped in Sandwich. You still with..."

'Nah, long gone, long gone mate, a year, more. What the fuck you doing in *Sandwich?*'

"Some jobs for a bit, good money. You still smoking?"

'It's the retirement plan.'

"I'll never give up."

'Yeah you will. We all do once.'

As if anyone needs to give up.
Have a word with yourself.
Have some self-control.
Defer some gratification.
Smoke less, this isn't the 70s. Five or ten a day does no harm and lots to enjoy.
Blam 20 on the lash take it easy a day or two.

Skilfully managed, most vices can last a lifetime and be sweet to the very last bite.

Apply the principle to pies and you won't need new big strides every six months after turning 40 neither. You don't want a stretchy waistband. Might as well stuff your head in the oven.

Read an article once, surgeon said as much about cigs. Be sensible, keep an eye on your wheezing, lay off during colds and/or other chestal infection, work a sweat up few times a week, don't get fat, like as not you're laughing kid.

Be 14 or 15 years ago now. Looked can't find it.

Probably electronically unhappened. They pay Google to forget.

Or the surgeon was in the pocket of Big Tobacco.

Or –

We've fallen out of objective history, if that place we ever were.

We thought we were the rolling stone, but we're the moss,

turning powerless on a tumbling rock, completely at a loss.

"Where's the smoking bit?"

'The street. We'll lose the chairs and my hip's throbbin'.'

"Aye, seen you limping peg-leg. Leave your coat."

'And lose my best coat in this fuckin' thief heap?'

"Don't look much, TK MAXX?"

'Yeah, there's some bargains to be had if you ain't a fat bastard.'

Reverse in fact the case though but.

Little for the middling man.

All end-of-line, basic maths.

We are the median, the mean,

In clover with an inside leg of 22 and 50 inch gut.

Best dressed circus freak ever seen.

"How much?"

'Thirty quid.'

"Seen you coming. Come on I'm dying for a fag."

Through the door, stop before you walk under a bus.
Smoking ban great for pubs lucky to have an existing outside or those holding
sufficient dough to create a plush smoking *experience* with shelter and heaters.
BigPubCo Charter.
Holes-in-the-wall left gasping on the kerb.
Oh spots of rain. Superb.
God knows pubs like this shithole would benefit from some smoke.
The more the better.
They'd benefit from being burned to the ground.
Sow the earth with salted peanuts.
But shrouding the clientele in haze'd be a start.
And it'd spare us the undertow of synthesized flowers.
How that ban hurt every small pub with bogs coming straight off the rooms.
As the smoke smell faded so rose the piss and fart.
And worse.
One time in this tiny Liverpool place, lovely nook, soon after the ban bit.
Snug, vault, bar, bogs, 30 bodies at a pinch could squeeze into it.
Lad slips off to snip off some putrefaction and by the time he returns to his
waiting girlfriend or missus or – best of all – first date, the deep rich aroma of
his droppings has penetrated every corner of the space, sizzling every nostril,
drawing forth dry heaves.
Red as beets the pair as they downed and took their leave, air still redolent of
the man's innermost bowels.
Poor bastard. But who shits on a night out anyway?
Piss would prove the pub-killer though, that relentless yellow river.
All you could smell in some, for a time, and in no time afflicted landlords waded
in with the plug-ins and every other format of air-freshener under the sun.
AirWick, Neutradol in the initial panic, barely tolerable brands,
but soon supplanted by the best you can find in Poundlands.

Cheapest going, as dawned the realisation that this is literally an issue which is never going away, would never be overcome.

A whole new long-term fixed cost to be met so long as the business model consisted solely of pouring gallons of fluid into people's bladders.

And thus the sickly chemical air now common to small pubs was born.

But not before we had glimpsed an important truth.

One ancient and ageless.

The piss had always been there. Is there still.

Centuries of heady chemical soup, hormonal hot and rich, has passed and been breathed. Only the camouflage has changed.

Woodbine to Jade Pine.

Take a night like this.

The Saracen's porcelain will be rinsed to the tune of, what – average a piss a pint per punter from four pint in, a pint of piss per piss, times 30-odd, that's four gallon an hour, probably 20 gallons of piss tonight.

Here's the thing though.

It's not just the new piss.

There's the old piss.

The history of piss, the pisstory, sunk and dried into every porous fabric of this building.

A living patina of degraded fuck and fight chemicals, daily replenished, refreshed, renewed and revived by said tide, another layer of active ingredients for the mix.

The message-laden ming, pungent vapour packed with communications for the inner ape, bypassing conscious thought, tickling nodes, alerting, warning, threatening, exciting, the swarming miasma, hanging in the air, infusing the curtains.

Sometimes, odd times, still, you briefly latch onto the tang, the acidic claw beneath the synthetic bouquet's glove.

The secret atmosphere of mass spoor.

And in this way people don't just make pubs, they mark pubs.

They take pubs.

Umpteen ways over time, breath, sweat, hot moist farts thumped into soft furnishings, but mostly through their urine.

Regulars yield a consistent river, chemical composition stable,

Piss of a Ted.

ebbing and flowing predictable as a tide-table,

from opening to time please,

falling back while the nation sleeps,

rising to torrent as it seeks refreshment, consolation, destruction.

In the Saracen's two centuries of drinking men – and an odd spouse or girlfriend, Friday night the lads, Saturday her, Sunday play by ear, put on your smarter gear – have turned wheaty fungal water into a million gallons of pheromone-laced acid, have slashed their elixir over cracked porcelain and tile, broken grout, unwitting boot and shoe, to tramp throughout, unwashed hands dab smear dab day in, day out, year in, year out.

Ask not for whom the bell-end drips.

It's not your bell-end.

It's their bell-ends.

A hundred thousand pints of potent territorial excretion a year down thirsty grates to conduits which hook this pile to the earth.

Grandad's piss, the piss of his peers,

the piss of their fathers, the piss of old dears,

piss of the dead of the wars picked out in black on gold in the rational edifice.

Piss of a Ted took twelve pints of heavy 1974

nodded off passed the lot in his jeans

through the carpet, into the wood floor,

drips in the cellar, between the flags, wets the sod.

Piss through the substance of the pub,

immune to minimum wage scrub,

and saturating the clay beneath,

via trough, crack and cranny,

seepage, osmosis, osmopis.

The old pubs create infused heath.

A column of impregnated steaming moor, plumes of decayed sex and violence greet every new ape through the door.

Smoking ban tore aside the veil.

And for a moment we were alone with the primal stank of ages.

Sacred piddle grounds.

You know those pubs where you never feel quite at ease?

Is all down to the piss.

8

Dark now, dark and drizzle.
Once saw Peter Kay in the drizzle.
He was turning on the lights.
Done that joke, crowd howled.
Meta.
The big lights.
Double.

"You got a light?"

'Yeah, found a brand new Clipper this afternoon.'

"How shit are Clippers now?"

'Free ones are alright.'

"There's no fucking gas in 'em."

Faint insistent from the distance, beyond the old pig-sty and courts, where the bright lights of this town such as they are begin and burn bright for 200 steps in any direction, comes the gathering sound of Saturday night action.
Rumbling bass, bawling lads, shrieking lasses.
But peaceful here, up the shit end in the shadow of the darkened market.
A scrawn shuffles out the side of the adjacent precinct.
Grimy trackie, head-down, hood up, hands deep in pockets, he stares in the window of the sub-Greggs pie-chain branch which, along with a low-rent bookies, this town's last sex shop and SLOTS O' FUN, welcomes shoppers to the Brehznev-era Soviet partially covered retail experience behind the locked iron gates.
Much vacancy, last I seen, a weigh-shop, rat shit in the muesli, MEGACIGS, esoteric charity shops, Poundmaster Plus, housing association office and

another amusement arcade on the way out.

Bingo hall on your right facing bus station, always a gaggle of smoking scooter-nans.

"What you doing with yourself then?"

'Writing a book.'

"For money?"

'It will be.'

"What about?"

'This town.'

"No cunt'll read that."

'Why not?'

"Who gives a shit about this town? I was born here and I don't.'

'Well it's about *more* than just this town.'

"It fucking wants to be."

'Have you read Hard Times?'

"No, but I've had a fuckin' few."

'Well Coketown, the town in that, was based on *this* town.'

"Oh right."

'Did you know that?'

"No."

'Dickens come here the year he wrote it, few month before he started. There was a big strike on, all the national news and that, and the book's about a strike, sort of a strike, in a town just like this town.'

"Your book is?"

'No his book was.'

"Is there any shagging in it?"

'There wasn't much call for shagging in books back then.'

"Not his book, yours."

'I'm thinking probably not.'

"I'd put a bit in if I was you, look at that Shades of Grey."

'I'm trying to prove this town was – is Coketown, look at how it's been played down and why it still is. There's no scope for shagging.'

"Pity. Why would anyone be arsed playing it down if nobody's heard of it?"

'That's *why* you ain't heard of it y'dick. Dickens put the boot in on all this town's great and good. Whole book is about how they're either corrupt, stupid, bastards, or all three.'

"Still are."

'Exactly, and my book will expl-'

"Scuse me asking lads, has either you got 52p please? Trying get back to Blackburn."

"Fuck off mate."

Ah this is the worst of the smoking ban.

Truth told, no problem getting up and moving about for a smoke. Even winter not averse to a wander, bit of fresh air, has helped me cut back an' all – but fucked if street smoking doesn't present moral dilemmas.

One small way in which non-smokers are that bit less engaged with reality. Brush up against it that bit less. Same reason only more so those who don't regularly use public transport.

They never have a fucking clue what's going on.

You get begged on the step every time, drinking in town. Every single time, sometimes several the one fag.

And I don't know what to do any more.

Easy when my income was good and secure,

flip them some smash.

Less easy in the biting wind of creative freedom.

I need that shrapnel for needful things, my copper and silver gets squeezed.

Got 10p mate?

Sorry mate, for some reason I've ended up trying to become a novelist. Well, they're sort of novels. Books. Niche, bit up myself some might say, but fairly well received. Can't get reviewed though, think I might have made enemies, so...

Budgeted to a degree you would not credit until the next royalty cheque, and already know that will be pathetic.

Once – don't lie, at least to yourself – *often* recently caught myself lie-thinking that I'm doing the poor fuckers a favour.

They'll only spend it on drink or drugs, and that ain't helping, and then I've squirmed in shame at myself, me, the fledgling pious bastard.

Am thinking instinctively out of financial impotence, I think and pray, a neurological coping reflex for status anxiety.

Because who deserves a drink or a bag more than a bag of bones trying get comfy in the hard angles of a draughty doorway?

I'd need a bottle of shorts at least to kip more than a blink.

'Sorry mate I ain't got no change.'

"Lyin' bastard! He's got a pocketful here mate!"

Tommo prods me right in the jingles.

'Fuck off eh? Look, sorry mate, I can't...'

"Anything you can spare'd be a help mate."

And he takes half a step forward at which Tommo gives him a big two-handed
shove in the tits and the kid flies back, a windmilling bundle of skin, sticks and
stained Umbro.
Catches his self right at the pavement edge, whirls his arms and leans way back,
as a mime might describe confronting a gale.
Righted he silently without a glance turns tail.

"See you again I'll spark you CUNT!"

'What the fuck're you doing, cock? People fall and split their fuckin' heads
open!'

"Wish he had, fuckin' beggars on the cadge all the time."

'They ain't at it from choice.'

"Course they are, don't be soft, not all of 'em do it. Look at that cunt over there,
he ain't got his hand out."

Waves his fag in the direction of the old Co-op. Nice building, windows
boarded, crumbling, biggest bit of art deco architecture in this town. Nothing
to write home about but decent. Marble-clad, in fair nick, or at least it was until
they left it to rot.
Doomed. I reckon gone soon.
Maybe there's an exciting leisure opportunity coming our way. A multiplex
boasting umpteen screens of non-stop shit for morons.
This town's first department store, opened in the 1920s, a caring sharing CWS

palace for the people. Pressed nose to glass every Christmas in childhood, coveting the toy display.

One year, one evening, a blue wet one near year's end, hand in gran's hand, I pointed out the Atomic Man and his many wondrous attributes.

Lo, his bulbous bonce appeared weeks later under coat hanger tinsel fir. Like magic.

There is a dark hump beneath the portico at the building's corner, close in near the door.

Rises a little, falls, rises and falls, rises, falls, rises – a hollow can slides off the human heap to kiss the ground with a shrill clatter – and falls.

'Nah look at the empties. He's hammered is all, or he'd be coppering round for the next four tins too. They're all over town the same now, poor bastards.'

"Well fuck him too. Fuck 'em all, lazy cunts."

'That could be you one day.'

"Don't talk shite."

'You never know what's round the corner.'

"I know I ain't a lazy cunt round the corner. You ready for another?"

'Fucking breaks my heart.'

"You should've give the nobhead a few quid then shouldn't you? *'Sorry mate'...*"

'I don't like to these days. Helping 'em buy booze and drugs and that ain't doing 'em no favours...'

Smouldering shame.

"Easy for you to say with your bed, I'd need to get battered non-stop, me, fuck it."

'Yeah, me an' all.'

"YOOOOUUUU CUUUUUUNTS!"

A tinny cry. Off down by the old dole, old dole where I signed the morning of my 16th birthday, couple of hundred yards, our shoved beggar yells and waves his arms.

"FUUUUCKIN' DOOO YOOOU CUUUUUNTS!"

Tommo chuckles, turns, heads for the bar.
I watch the boy faintly offer us out, slowly finish my fag.
Poor sod still working to reclaim dignity as I step back inside the Saracen's Head.

A hollow can slides off the human heap to kiss the ground.

9

"Cheers."

What's this scum-fizz?

'What the fuck is this?'

"Lager."

'I was on Stella.'

"You said you hated Stella."

'I do but I'll take it over Black fuckin' Label.'

"Yeah it's gnat's piss."

'Gnat's piss through a SodaStream.'

"Ha ha."

'Cheers then.'

"Ha ha. Here, remember that skeleton tramp outside Debenhams about 20 year ago with the whistle?"

'Yes, he's still there.'

"He's still fuckin' there! Looks like fuckin' Catweazle now with the hair."

'Lost his whistle thank fuck.'

Spot him few time a week, few steps along from the newsagents.

That stretch of flags been the stage where he's played out his whole life.

But never could play that fucking whistle, though plied it years on end.

He moved his fingers randomly over the holes and blew.

Well I say randomly, but it was always the same tune.

Doodly-oodly-oooo-doodly-oodly-oooo-oodly-oooo-doodly-oodly-oooo...

Same notes, sequence, over and over, slower over winter, fingers freezing.

For a time passed him twice daily, workbound homebound morning evening.

Doodly-oodly-oooo-doodly-oodly-oooo-oodly-oooo-doodly-oodly-oooo...

Heard that tune so often I hear it still.

Eventually made me question free will.

Waggle your fingers randomly.

Stop.

Again.

Stop.

Again.

Stop.

That's how you waggle your fingers when you think 'waggle fingers randomly'.

Every time.

Try again, holding a penny whistle to your lips, blow.

Doodly-doooooo-doodly-deeeeee-ooodly-doodly-doooooo-doodly-deeeeee...

That's the hardwired penny whistle theme tune of your machine self.

Unless you know how to play, which messes with the experiment.

Doodly-doooooo-doodly-deeeeee-ooodly-doodly-doooooo-doodly-deeeeee...

"You know that fat Paki rides up and dow-"

'Please don't talk that fucking shit round me mate.'

"Fat?"

'Why would I give a fuck about fat, you're the fat cunt. Paki. Paki. You don't even believe all that bollocks neither.'

"What bollocks?"

'All that Nigel fuckin' Farage bollocks.'

"Why is it bollocks?"

'Cos he's a fuckin' privately educated toff bastard playing people with fuck all against each other. He wouldn't piss on you if you was on fire.'

"Just cos he's made a bit of money don't mean he don't get it."

'Get what? There's fuck all to get.'

Ding ding, all change.
Mother Nature's bigot of old filed any and every politician under *cunt* as a collective, as one body, no distinction or debate, deemed exactly as unTommo as some bloke fresh off the boat.
Something cut through.
Overcome reservations,
focussed detestations.
Pushed the right buttons,
pulled the right levers,
lit the fire and stuck a poisonous bun in the oven.
Ping.
One large white believer, hot to trot, ready to slice.
Another. I have family who once or twice...
What you meant to do when these people – those you are emotionally saddled with, by blood or time – start to swing far far further and further right under the indignity and pain of age?
Piss away your time on their impotent rage?
You get more right wing as you get older
is the common lie-excuse
but only true where youthful views
were less about faith in fairness
and more about getting balls wet, yes?
Why can't everyone share,
wept secret Tory student at party on stair.

Because who is going to fuck a Tory but another Tory and there's none there.

Or they're all hiding like you.

Age reveals, it never changes.

Time wears masks as waves wear rock.

Depths revealed as surface becomes sand on the wind.

And lately lots of middle-to-late-middle-aged English men are revealed as venomous.

But how far is too far?

What to forgive in kith and kin?

Where exactly to draw the line?

Or better just to bear and grin?

Take the piss? Lock antlers?

Try to save them?

Teach the error of their ways, dig out the kinder soul you've missed of late, was it ever present? Must be or how come they're your granddad or mate?

Save them from themselves, you think,

in your fucking arrogance, they think.

And once all fails, as it must, the gentle non-parting parting.

Meet now and then, pay lip service, less and less, blessed infrequent reunions unto death.

Unless you're sweating on a will of course,

And who hasn't a few quid on that horse?

And on the way to then, until that blessed last goodbye, if snared in their presence?

Deflect.

'So what about the fucker then?'

"That one rides round in the electric chair comes screwing-up wanting cash and fags if you sit down outside for ten second."

'I know him, he's a fucking pain in the arse.'

"I've sat down in town about three times since I got back and he's drive-byed us twice."

I know him, he's a fucking pain in the arse.

'I reckon he's a bit simple.'

"Well I'm coming down from the station and about hundred yard up outside Bodycare there's this black lad talking to a little old Paki woma-"

'Will you fuck off with that shit?'

"And this black lad starts shouting his head off and legs it toward Ann Summers."

Erotic window displays dispensing tingles at the corner of Town Hall Street since 1999.

"He's after that Paki who's —"

'Fuck off.'

"— head down nearly out of sight right down the end. This black lad's like shit off a shovel though, tags him and this big row kicks off, him yelling and waving his arms about! Thought he was going to belt him. I gets down to the old Pak-"

'Fuck off.'

I should walk, that'd feel briefly good.
Two fingers and "it was nice to chat".
But such performative gesture only tells this lot they've won, so bollocks to that.
Wait, bide your time.
Make him look cunt enough once we hook up with the lads. Better with an audience.

"-i and goes what's the crack and she reckons how that cunt in the chair's had a few quid out of this lad but he's not on his arse at all and *never has been.* Lives round her, nice house, benefits, walks about happy as Larry in his yard once he's done his rounds round town, and she's jumped out of Bodycare when she seen him begging this black lad."

'Arsehole.'

"This black lad was walking back and he goes to me don't give that snide bastard nothing, he's a con-man, and I goes no fucking chance pal."

'There are some snide bastards about.'

"They're all at it."

'Some of 'em.'

Some of 'em *are* at it, a few of 'em are at it, no point lying to yourself.

"All of 'em."

Doesn't mean it ain't tragic for all concerned, for them, for us, for civilisation.
For everyone tired of living amid casualties, of having our nose rubbed in our shit and as yet unwilling or unable to develop the instinctual salvation of looking away.
It just means there's one or two bullshitters.
Junkies and cidermen most,
those with a need
they need to feed,
which pays dignity no heed.
Bad apples spoiling the barrel of acceptable misery.
If you think it's a cushy number be my guest.
Been sanctioned a lot of the new kids on the block paving, otherwise undoled on some technicality, or because they took the piss, or fell off the system, or are stupid or fried and missed an appointment.
System's deliberately hard for the chaotic individual,
but come on, set a fucking alarm, be half punctual.
Yet they each have all my sympathies.
Even dickheads born looking for an excuse.

Because aren't we all?
Question only of what you aim to excuse.
Things you did or things you didn't?
We're all at it.

'A few of 'em.'

"More than half."

'How in fuck do you magic up the number that it's more than half?'

"It's obvious."

'It's balls. And how come there ain't a black lad *and* an Asian lad in your story?'

"Eh? There was, the angry lad got begged."

'Yeah, but how come he ain't the n-word?'

"You politically correct now then? The n-word…"

Fuck I should have said it then and swallowed the awful taste.
He knows I've said it before, when and where.
A stupid smalltown kid and ignorance in the air.
Lot of skins about too.
Made in Britain, 1982.
Clash and Bragg steered me from Hell.
Only Tommo liked Joe and Billy as well.
That's me tagged in his head as a self-censoring wet-end.
There is a policeman inside all our heads and mine is destroying my precious
free speech, even in private conversation, he thinks.
Libtard snowflake, a gift to trigger
betrayed through due reluctance
to bandy the word nigger.
This is not a bad thing.

It is the right thing.

I did the right thing.

He did the wrong thing.

But you lack such luxury one-on-one with the Tommos of this world.

They equate decency as weakness or complicity,

two parts PC mind control, three parts pure naivety,

and thus armed they'll happily muddy waters all day.

You're in a ditch.

Better to blanch inside, bite your cheeks and defuse their few crude weapons on contact.

Straight back in their face it will not reappear.

Unless you're black, in which case knock them the fuck out.

"Niggers are alright, they ain't trying blow us to fuck."

'*We* blow everyone to fuck.'

"We ain't driving trucks over kids."

'No we're fuckin' droppin' buildings on kids with two hundred thousand quid bombs, burying the cunts alive to suffocate or die of thirst or internal bleeding, nice and slow.'

"Most of 'em it'd be quick."

'Some take days.'

"I've heard you're full-on tripping at the end with suffocation."

'Hence auto-erotic asphyxiation.'

Gasping pressed in black,

wondering where mum is,

when dad's coming back,

can't they hear your cries?

Dust falls in your eyes,
and distant scraping fades.

"Who was that singer died of a strangle-wank?"

'There's been a few.'

"I met a bird liked being throttled."

'How did that that come up?'

"It was on her bio."

'You digital sexcase.'

"She asked us to throttle her."

'I don't think I could.'

"It was alright. You going the bar? I'll have a Guinness if it's back on."

How'd you end up getting off being throttled?
Throttled and banged by a bigot?

Gasping pressed in black.

10

'Is Guinness back on?'

"Guinness ain't coming back on we had one of them surprise visits."

'Always thought that was an urban myth.'

"Eh? So Derek reckoned. Said a bloke come Tuesday said they'd been Monday have a pint and we was damaging the brand. Went down the cellar took a thing off and now the tap don't work."

'Two Stella.'

"Beamish is better anyway."

'No it ain't.'

Don't be a fucking idiot.
Beamish? Bollocks.
Not bad, but it's not that.
Nothing is better than Guinness. Nothing is more reliable in this life.
And I mean nothing.

"Seven forty mate."

'Put the change in your box.'

Ten pee bigshot.
Can't knock that for two Stella.

"No Guinness?"

'Off for good, had one of them spies in from head office.'

"What spies?"

'Secret Guinness agents slip in and buy pints. If you're fuckin' it up they cut you off just like that.'

"My arse, that's balls."

'I've heard stories like it but I'd always thought it was bullshit.'

"It is bullshit. Freehold this ain't it? Probably fell behind. One I went in Deal run out of vodka one Saturday night, cracked on it's a mistake. Boards up two week later."

'Deal?'

"Near Sandwich."

'Where the fuck is Nye?'

"He says he'll be an hour. Good health."

'Eh? When?'

"Text when you was at the bar, he's held up with the kids."

Fucking hell Nye.
Bloody kids.
Lucky Nye.
They must come first.
When you're alone you've only yourself to think about. That and the failings of others.

"You had any kids?"

'No, so who else is meant to be coming here then?'

"Fuck knows, you still with that lass?"

'Nah, I told you before, Nye said Pete was coming here.'

"Yeah but Pete rung me said he was out later."

'I rung you about ten times, you never picked up.'

"He's picking up Kecks and Butch."

'Big Butch?'

"Didn't say."

'Won't be Little Butch.'

Their dad was a butcher.

"Fucking hope not."

'Won't be, ain't seen him this decade. Never knocked about proper any road, tagalong. They coming here?'

"He got in touch with us at Facebook in Sandwich, Little Butch, he was after a nip down, but I'm fuck that, smackhead."

'He was good for cheap meat, our kid got a carrier bag full of steak off him, five quid. They coming here?'

"Bull about nine."

Dickens' digs.

'Might as well fuck off there after these, is gone eight.'

"I don't mind this. Three-seventy Stella? You pay that in Wetherspoons."

'Let's fuck off there then, is only over from the Bull. I'll text Nye.'

Dirty Wetherspoons, Wankerspoons, but better than this place.
Filling up and every side an angry wounded face.
Aggrieved not cut, though enough of them too.
Don't blame them, they've been beaten down,
but I still want out their sacred space in town.
Their ureal temple of malevolence, male violence.
Still the one bird but now 40, 50 fellas.
And her a pissed-up squawking mess,
all between us and a blood sausage-fest.
Yowling on the arm of her brooding goon,
later 'boot his head' from cab rank step
while feet draw red under a blue moon.
Set out to shun 'spoons soon as that wanker got politics under his mullet and
started putting nationalist agitprop out at Curry Club.
He turned the breakfast pinters against us, the Full English sots.
Trouble is, nobody else will do you a double good rum, not your Lamb's Navy
crap, and free mixer, for the same you'd pay for a single anywhere outside a
working men's club.
Will they though?
So what'd you do?
In hard times?
Wind in your neck,
suck up the value.
Easier, the principled stand
when one has cash in hand.
But there are other excuses, professional excuses.
We writers must keep abreast of how people talk.
You people.
We writers.

Feet draw red under a blue moon.

How you say what you say more than what you say.

Hardly anyone hardly ever says a solitary thing of interest or worth, to jot down and jog home and pop in the mouth of a fictional soul.

Myself included. Mostly hear the shit from my mouth and think 'arsehole'.

No, rhythms and patterns alone are gold next to the thin pickings of content.

And nowhere better than 'spoons.

Unfortunately for my conscience.

Silence, you see. Big open rooms,

always fairly busy, never any tunes.

Although some turn into discos weekend nights.

Find a spot and open your ears to the banal chorus of human conversation.

Public transport also a source.

Less trains, carriages can be quiet.

More middle-class of course.

Buses far more lively, up to and including the odd riot.

The bussing classes hide less shout more.

Heard this one story up a double-decker one summer morning on the way to work ten or so years ago.

Better than gold.

"Can do."

'Fucker won't reply though, he never does.'

But then neither do I.

"Once I've met this lad."

'What lad?'

"The lad am meeting here. Should've been here already."

'Meeting why?'

"He's doing us a favour."

Powder. Always the sort. Gob ego. The drug chooses you.

'Ahhh, a favour of some lovely cocaine.'

"Fuck off, I don't touch that shit."

Or maybe not. Knew he'd dabbled, we probably dabbled together, but never a heavy user of anything much past drink, even weed.

"Been a year this Christmas."

Knew it.

"He's doing me a favour."

'When'd he say he's bringing your sweet cocaine?'

"Should've been and gone."

Shouldn't we all?

11

"So I was sunbathing on the trampoline in that new bikini and this corn-cob comes over the fence nearly hits our kid and his mates. That Kano picks it up and throws it back and there's this horrible scream, kid screaming his head off. I sticks my head over the fence and this fat kid's got blood down his face from his eye screaming and they're having a birthday party, garden's full of kids and balloons. That stupid bitch from the Spar wouldn't serve us that time picks up the corn-cob and shouts 'Who threw corn-cob?' it looks like it's her kid, and I goes 'You threw corn-cob it nearly hit our kid' and I looks round and him and his mates have legged it inside and the fat bitch is climbing on a chair shouting 'Who threw corn-cob?' over the fence trying to look, and there's about four big fat bitches in the garden now shouting and kids screaming and I goes 'You threw fuckin' corn-cob!' and she jumps down and runs into her house. I'm still arguing with them fat cows then there's banging –"

The girl, who is perhaps 19 or 20, clenches her left hand into a fist and mimes, thump thump thumping, a fist overarm against a door.
She is alone and speaking into a telephone.
I am three seats back.
Right hand busy in my lap.
Notebook and pen not wanking.
Although she was a pretty girl.
Dirty old bastard. Although I was still in my 30s at the time so...
Bikini reference likely what hooked me onto the story from the get-go.
Am all ears. What next for the bikini-clad blonde?
Nobody is any different.
You're certainly not.

"– bang bang bang at the front. I go the door and our kid's behind the sofa and I'm still in me bikini, and the kid's dad's there, big fat get, and that bitch and the cow from next door and the fat get's shouting in that he knows our kid's in there and he's going to have him and the bitch is 'Who threw fucking corn-cob?' and I'm in the street, still in me bikini, 'You threw fuckin' corn-cob!' for about an hour. I've gotta get off, bye."

Phone in her bag she disembarked.
Closed my notebook, wondered what to make of it all.
Thought about her in her new bikini on the trampoline.
I was very fucking high.

Who threw corn-cob?

12

"How come they've put Noel Edmonds on all the bandits now?"

'I was thinking that before.'

"Pub I drunk down there had two bandits and both had him on. Towed one away, brung another, and that had the cunt on too."

'He has a big constituency among the afternoon viewers.'

"They're fuckin' mad now have you seen 'em? Not 10p a spin any more."

'How fucked would Mick be? He'd be fuckeder than ever if he was still on that shite.'

Mick always first in Castle.
There when you rolled in, glowering at the bandit, pint of lager top up top,
barely licked, bought mainly to change a note into metal for the slot.
You get a drink and watch the reels spin while he explains how it's about to drop,
how X amount has gone in, and why Y amount must therefore be due,
and weird, that melon usually comes down the middle if you hold them two.
Twice.
Someone else rocks up to join the vigil, then someone else, then another,
then someone gets a table and you take a pew, and Mick says, I'll be over in a minute or two.
It's just about to drop.
And then he's again alone with the machine.
Although they're always alone with the machine.
And then that's him for the duration.
Two, three, four, lonely necked flat pints, which had sat untouched atop his tormentor an hour or a half or 2 minutes, depending on the whim of the maw.
Repeat until pockets flapping.

We'd all been there.

Varying degrees of bandido slapping.

Misspent childhoods three deep round taxi rank Kung Fu Masters and filling the fruits for cabbies to empty once the seedy bastards decided to boot us into the night, try a few pee.

Game changer once fit to pass in offies and pubs, childish things put sharpish away, scarce pennies scraped aside for Friday and Saturday.

And maybe this made us a bit cold. A bit blasé.

We'd sort of try.

We'd stop by on the way to or fro bar or trough and 'for fuck's sake Mick, don't sling all your dough in that cunt again, we're having a laugh'.

But if you know those people you know it's always about to drop.

So you'd watch a bit, not long, have a smoke, oooh, that was close.

But inevitably, you're 19, it's Friday, them lasses from the college just rolled in half-cut and that one I seen looking at me on the bus last week is there and she just looked at me now and smiled so, with the best will in the world, Mick, fuck this shit I'm off.

And you'd glance over an hour later and a pint'd be there on top, a sip or two down, and a sliver of Mick in flickering light, and you'd look over an hour after that and either nothing had changed or there'd be a lacy glass awaiting collection and no Mick.

Some other illuminated face testing its luck.

Mick slipped away, that's how it went. All the way home, 8pm Saturday, best gear on, Brut still exuding, teasing and tormenting his self, as you do, as any addict of anything will tell you.

Must have been 30 years old before he got clear, from hooking on in early teens. Escaped just in time to grow old.

Missed making so many of the memories which keep us warmest when we start to feel the cold.

"There was a bloke in Sandwich same, well old though, 60-odd, 70, and smart looking, always ties. He was wanking his wallet into one of that pub's bandits like clockwork every single time I had a pint there."

'Addiction makes people clockwork.'

"When he was on a downer he'd be talking to it, muttering at it, 'you are taking the *piss*', thrashing the nudges when there's no win. But every time he got a jackpot he'd be like turning round to us all like nodding and smiling as if it was something he'd done while the quids blasted out."

'That big thunk thunk thunk ain't needed. It's for us, catch our attention to the riches, and for them, in their minds, they think we're all looking. They think everyone in the pub has an eye on their struggle and cares.'

"Then he stops coming in. Never seen him months on end, everyone thinks he's dead, fucking jumped off a cliff or summat. Suddenly one night there he is, slapping as per. Hard he's at it, playing fast, must've cracked eight tenners, throwing it in, machine-gunning the buttons like Daley Thompson long jump, raging he was, *'you are taking the piss'* spitting it."

'Seen Mick like that a bit.'

I seen Mick giving fruit machines a sneaky dig. A kick, a slap, as if they could feel. As if there were some reciprocal relationship between he and the device, as if he could hurt it the same way its lifeless processes were hurting him.
But we've all had fights with objects.
All been Fawlty with the tree.
That's why it's funny, do you see?
Speaks to buried spirituality for me.
Squeezed deep in the human psyche,
investing dead matter with vengeful agency.

"Next this old bag and a bird rush in, looking around, then they spot him and they're going how they've been worried, and looking for him, but you could see they weren't angry they were heartbroken. And he's seen 'em coming and steps back from the bandit, face like this, all calm and smiling like this, like he's just had a shit after holding it an hour, and he goes 'Ohhhh I needed that'."

'Noel flashing in the background.'

Ohhhh I needed that.

"Oh I needed that. Like he's had a fuckin' treat, like he was back off his holidays!"

'How come you ended up in Sandwich?'

"Her sister was near. Never seen the poor bastard again."

'Maybe he found that cliff.'

"Yeah. So who's going to read a book about this town?"

'I – it's not really about this town. More about politics and memory, history and stuff.'

"Politics and history and stuff of this town?"

'Yeah but only... They're universal in their...'

"How's that not about this fucking town then?"

'Meaning...'

Of course the book will only superficially be about this town. Solely as case study from which to draw clear conclusions applicable to wider themes, not as a thing itself.
Two distant distinct but related historical events and how efforts to control and manage their aftermath continue to this day more than 160 years later.
In the context of Brexit maybe. That'll be good for sales.
Maybe don't even let on it is this town.
Until right at the end.

'But I ain't *telling* them that it is about this town, that's the thing. The plan is to change all the street names, the pubs, everything.'

"Why?"

'Except the murdered men's names. They'll be like a key. People who know will know at once, people who don't know but care about the principles will stick with it. People like a mystery.'

"What murdered men?"

In fact, they don't. If people liked mystery they wouldn't be so keen to resolve them. They view mysteries as threats or targets.
Billions have detested mystery so much they swallowed God to make it go away.

"Do it like them CSI, there's fucking hundreds of them now."

'CSI Ambleside. My old dad watches the lot, records 'em. Every time I'm up there now he's watching some fucker elbow deep in guts and shit.'

"You know where you are with them, step by step. Your book sounds hard work."

'It will be hard work, but life shouldn't always be ice cream.'

"People like ice cream."

'I like fucking ice cream, but people like Marmite too don't they?'

"Not many."

'I reckon people into Dickens will have a look too.'

"You'd better hope so."

'And politics junkies. It's going to be full of politics and there's shitloads of people thinking themselves that now.'

Chatting shit, the lot.
Why would you want to be a junkie of any description?
Known enough junkies to know that depth of dependency on any external

force is going to make for an unhappy and ultimately corrosive state of being.
You often see
political junkie
turn out to be
grim prophecy.
Initial rush over, thrill into drab fixation,
wellspring of woe, depression, frustration,
ranting impotent, mental deterioration.
Who was it said to understand the world you had to look away?

'Middle-aged middle classes are bang into politics again, this the first time it's
fucked them over in years.'

"I've seen them *Remoaners* marching on telly."

'Did you see that dick bat whose dog is sad it won't be able to ski? They're
fighting for retirement to Provence at 50.'

"I want to punch the fuck out of most of them."

'Me too, but same time I don't at all. They're decent people and I agree with a
lot of what they say, they've just had good jobs nice lives and their heads up
their own arseholes so long they don't have a fuckin' clue what a cuntfire this
country's been for 30 year.'

"Is it my round?"

'Half politics junkies were born small hours of June 24th 2016.'

Epiphany is useful as tits on a tree if the moment has passed.
This one struck when a sinking ship they'd been up the dry end of lifted her
propeller out the water broke in half and began sinking fast from the arse.
Icy brine in the nostrils no way to be woken after a long and comfortable sleep.
In shock they see politics as it was last time they glanced. Soundbites, a series
of black and whites, for us, against us.

Politics not as unknowable collision-flux of culture, history, philosophy, economics, iconography, faith, media, ideas of selfhood, everything, every mashed up fucking aspect of human cognisance, no, as litany of unrealistic and conflicting yes-no demands, usually issued under tacit threat of propping up bastardy.

I still think they'll usher in the final act.

Politics is not cosmic ordering, just ask Noel Edmonds.

"What happened then?"

'When?'

"June the... 2016."

'The EU vote.'

"Oh yeah, ha ha, I voted to fuck off me."

'Well stripe me pink, what a surprise.'

"Bob Geldof is a cunt."

'You're a cunt, and yes it is your round.'

He is a cunt.
But he's right about Bob Geldof.

13

'Cheers.'

"Those about to wife-beat we salute you!"

Top of his voice like. Pair of Ogdens next table glance over.
Tommo laughs. They laugh. He laughs. I don't laugh.
Happy to play along to keep a Glaswegian from biting my face, but that pair of blotchy ruins couldn't beat an egg.

'Yes, good health.'

"Never knew why Stella got that rep, me."

'A lot of angry hardened drinkers drink it then take out their pain and failure on loved ones.'

"Bobby's dad knocked fuck out of him on Spar cider most days."

'Am joking, it's just Stella's bad luck. First strong foreign beer come in pints wasn't it? Sent us all fucked unrivalled for years until the rest come along.'

"Remember when they first put Heineken Export on at Castle?"

'You couldn't go for a piss without getting dragged into a scrap.'

"I'd kill that cunt now if he wasn't dead. He had a swing at me when I was 8 or summat, I'm trying drag Bobby out..."

'Bobby and his brother smashed the cunt's grave up, did he ever tell you?'

"Ha ha, aye. About a week after the funeral that. Reckon he'll be out tonight?"

'Sure he'll hop on a flight from Brisbane for a pint in this pox crater.'

"Is that where he's at now?"

'About ten year. Christ I could go a Guinness…'

"I can't usually be arsed waiting."

'Some waits are better than others.'

It's the open-ended waits for uncertain outcomes you want to avoid.
Long as you know what you're waiting for, roughly how long before it'll show…
Some waits are a chance to learn, if we recognise and take them.
Missed a bus by seconds one Sunday, limped to the stop just in time to watch
its arse slide from view.
The first Sunday, in fact, after England's World Cup semi-final loss.
Half hour until the next so a comfy pint in nearby Silver Cross.
Short hop stop to step, so in ordering Guinness before the bus has changed up
out the turn. Next thing bloke along bar is on me like an hungry shithouse rat.
We're similar age. He's shorter, five-ten, around, solid though, bristled skull,
grown-out skin, cold blue eyes, well-bashed face, trapful of teeth cracked and
AWOL.
Halfway down a lager, four or five fingers, clearly keen to chat and up in my
grille before the barman, a sprat of a lad who'd be no use, has even put the
change in my hand.
Two-thirds pulled the boy flips up the stout tap and we await the settle.
Agenda, item one, no preamble, straight in, by way of introduction, profoundly
pissed off by the recent World Cup.
He's glad England got beat.
He wants to know if I'm glad.
I say I don't know.
He's fucking glad it's all over.
He can't stand how they analyse everything before during and after the match.
What the fuck are they talking about? If he'd done this that'd have happened
but he didn't so what's the fucking use going on?

I agreed, sincerely, not from fear of this agitated and clearly aggressive man, although I remained up on the balls of my feet, but because he was right. And I wondered how my then recently diagnosed and acutely painful hip would stand up to whatever came next.

Staked out more common ground, saying there should only be one commentator in the box, because soon as the game flags a bit the dickheads start prattling shit at one another. And over time they've gradually forgot why they're there in the first place, and so now they sometimes prattle shit at one another even when the game ain't flagging.

What the fuck are they talking about, he says, then rephrases this sentiment several times, angrily. Gently nudging my elbow with his glass hand each time he thinks, presumably, he has offered some qualification or insight to which I should pay full attention.

Which is often. Nudge nudge nudge.

Three kinds of people do that.

Nutters, pricks and pricks who are nutters.

"Are you glad England got beat?"

'I don't know mate.'

Humouring him, watching that Guinness settle.

He's been drinking at home a few weeks because he hates the World Cup and the pubs've been full of wankers. The hangovers get him down.

"I get down, in myself, mate."

By now Guinnessed am getting that down in myself.

"All these fucking idiots coming out watch the games are after is a scrap."

'I ain't watched much out to be fair.'

"I fucking hate all that me."

'That's why I watch at home.'

Watched the semi-final in a pub. Set out indifferent but by the end willing their defeat, wanting it heavy, purely to upset the pricks there gathered.
Which I suppose makes me quite a small man.

"Who'd they think they are?"

I go aye, people are too wound-up and full of their selves these days. We all need to chill a bit.
Guinness slipping away like milk thank Christ.
He don't understand it, what the fuck are they analysing, and prods my chest with his glass-hand as he speaks.
He can't be arsed with fighting.

"You into that sort of shit are you mate?"

And I'm nah, at my age? Stout goes perpendicular, good health mate, out the door, ham the limp, walking past the bus stop on the doorstep to the next a quarter mile on.
A stop full of coleslaw, doner shreds and blue plastic chip forks.
What did I learn?
They do a nice Guinness in the Silver Cross.
Told our kid who said I should have chinned him. Told him never to throw first punch at cunts look like they've had a scrap every week this century. And how I'd be brawling every third pint if approaching me while being a headcase was the criteria.
The poor fuckers like me. They pick me out of crowds, seek me out, tell me about themselves, always have, not sure why.
Then again such meets mightn't be rare
if you frequent pubs before noon,
because they're always there,
the unmoored lads and lasses,
nursing grievances and glasses.
Saturday morning just gone in the 'spoons – research – no sooner had my arse

touched beer garden seat than one was at my side explaining himself, laying out the facts of who and what he was and places he'd been, things he'd done and seen.

This is my life.

Asked nothing of mine,

so nothing volunteered.

Didn't seem to mind.

Burly six footer big beard.

Lank long black hair. Sleeveless T-shirt despite the chill, uninspired partial sleeves.

A fresh head wound, two inches or so in length, snaking up from the right eyebrow.

Maybe in his 30s, maybe in his 20s, without knowing his poisons hard to say.

Whatever these poisons his manner hinted he'd been wide awake and using them for many many hours.

Eyes all over, red-rims, bright then dim and back, roving left, right, in and out of focus.

He spoke, I muttered, a nod, a yeah here, a nah there, watchful.

He's rambling and always that bit too close to be comfortable.

Shared his scars, literal scars, lifted his shirt for the stranger, traced puckered lines across his paunchy trunk with a thick finger.

Manchester Arena, he said, the bomb.

I was at the concert, wasn't I?

The scars were neat and old, faint ellipses, five or six inches, either side of the abdomen. To my layman's eye they screamed surgical,

long healed precision, incisions symmetrical.

But flesh splits funny, so what do I know man?

Nothing.

Though he didn't look like no Ariana Grande fan.

Said South Manchester born and bred, sounded too posh. Cheshire?

He went to school with the bomber, didn't believe that either.

Bomber wasn't religious, he goes, not at all.

He liked a smoke, and I know Muslims that do,

but this one liked a drink too.

He had no ideology, was just a bad person, no cause, just hate.

As if those things are mutually exclusive.

Suicide is an option, he goes, out of the blue,

you don't have to be here, do you?

And I thought no but this is where we keep all our stuff, but didn't voice my sneers, because he had four stone on me easy and appeared to be on the brink of tears.

So I goes, 'Life's what you make it'.

He said he loved philosophy and I nodded and he insisted he loved philosophy, and outlined his personal philosophy and it was all alt-fashionable cul-de-sac, a meme brainshat which amounted to nothing, betrayed nothing but his inability or unwillingness to think with even a stab at detachment.

He loves philosophy.

The best wise quotes.

Even when I'm with someone I feel alone, he goes, and I said you are but that's okay so is everyone, and always will be, so you might as well learn to enjoy it for what it is.

He asked what it is and I said I don't fucking know lad, and he clammed up at last.

Dinked my fag, downed my pint, wished him luck and strolled, first irked but soon grateful a desired quiet moment had been disturbed.

I didn't get to take pause and reflect.

But I did get a peek inside someone else's head and a few words for this book.

'In Ireland they have them piled-up half-pulled on the go all night.'

"This ain't Ireland though."

'If you know roughly how long you'll wait it ain't waiting it's just patience.'

"I've none of that neither."

'Patience's fell out of fashion since we fucked God off.'

What value has time on the threshold of eternity?

A mere countdown, length irrelevant to the grand finale.

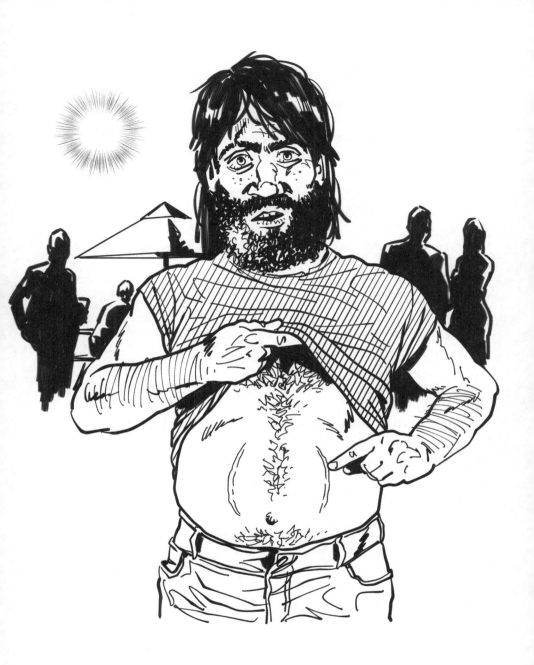

I was at the concert, wasn't I?

Am amazed we still queue,
still say 'after you',
hangover of immortality passed.
Post-war science education taught the massed
pleb ranks they were momentary.
Time has no price now, everybody knows.
Patience? Out of the window that goes.
You be patient, soppy bastard, I'm already in my tomb,
life is a chute to the void not Heaven's waiting room.

'Give your tardy dealer a bell, tell him meet you in the Bull.'

"It ain't *coke* and I ain't got a number. I don't know the cunt at all, he's meant to be calling me when he gets here."

'Well if he ain't rung by the bottom of this pint I'm off meeting them lot, it's quarter to.'

"He'll be here, I ain't paid yet."

Opens coat to flash a thick tit-pocket wad, looked a ton-odd or thereabout.

'Fuck off, what do you spend that much on if not powder?'

"It ain't, but I can get some if you want some."

'I'm 50, who can be arsed? Can you get hold of hashish?'

"You still have a blend?"

'For my aching bones.'

"Gives me headache. I can get you some green."

'Anyone can get me some green, I'm after black, that old sticky black. I'd give a bollock and an inch of cock for a steady lump of that sticky black used to get.'

Green ain't the same, barely comparable.
Can be trickled to ape the mild insistence
of gentle block buzz but less predictable
and easy to trip into nonsense.
Seldom the same sort twice and can be half through a bag before the dosage
is defined. And then a slip, a pinch over, a careless drunkard's crumble, that's
you out your mind.
Bonced and gawping, at screen or sheet, scrawling, typing, crossing out,
selecting all, backspace.
Want a step back and to the side, an angle,
not to run my neurons through a mangle.
Plus hip and sundry pains to wrangle.
But hash is a labour-intensive product, lengthy, involved, stinking, historically
mostly undertaken outside Britain then smuggled in.
Big faff.
More bodies, more pressure points, less control, complicated supply line,
complexity equals risk and risk hits the main line, the bottom line.
Viable on the continental land mass,
movement less a pain in the arse,
as it was here, for all the tribulation,
prior to the hydroponics revolution.

'Hash got killed by technology. Anyone can set their selves up with state-of-
the-art kit cheap and turn out a cash-crop now. I've thought about it.'

"I thought they'd legalised it anyhow, ages back, 90s."

'Nah, changed law for minor possession in case sons of Ministers and the
liberal rich get pulled in Soho with half a 'teenth is all. Slapped wrist for Toby
and Seb if the fucking slags'll grass who helped 'em. Same time brought down
what you need be holding to be a dealer, and outside big cities some pigs
started going hard after small fry. Old hippy in the sticks used to help me out
round the Millennium retired because he got bored of his fucking door coming

through every second week. He did about half a nine-bar a month, solely for mates and his own free smoke.'

"Have you tried that spice?"

'Do I look like a fuckwit?'

"Yeah."

'If I get that desperate I'll try 200 paracetamol and a litre of rum.'

Spice is a nightmare just begun.
Such things we're going to see.
Clocked one lad last week having fun.
Never clocked a human in a worse state and I seen smackheads when the hit lands.
Lengthy droughts push you into realms of the cursed.
We were waiting on four ounces, they got seen to first.
Spice boy was perched on a low wall off the square, rocking, legs spread, feet flat, trunk leaning right back, 45 degrees, every atom of him wriggling at once.
Slit eyes staring out the sun.
Softly gibbering,
monosyllabic babbling,
mantra too low to hear.
Liverpool last year midweek city centre, busy as, watched two lads battle in the road with scaffolding poles over alleged spice theft.

'Spice is death. Small towns, kids wanting a smoke, can't afford a proper deal even if they knew a dealer, no old hippies happy to do 'teenths now.'

"Remember them 'teenths off Jimmy? Matchsticks. Seven quid, two spliffs."

'Kills people straight off time to time, drag or two, poofff, multiple organ fuckage.'

"The nicks are full of it."

'Half every cunt getting out has the taste. Godber'd be a babbling psycho vegetable if he was in Slade today.'

"He'd have battered Fletch to death then hung himself with his kecks."

The puritan right secretly cherish spice,
the public indignity, that vengeful kill rate.
Warnings to the curious, you play nice.
They'd hang them from lampposts, signs round their necks,
repent sinners, it's already too late.

"Got to be fuckin' thick to smoke the shit though, so it's no big loss."

'There was two nice middle-class students killed off it 20 mile up the road not long back.'

"Yeah well we're not short of them cunts neither. I'd legalise everything."

'Some rural dream they lived in – Me too but governments in charge won't fix nothing. Look at booze, look how they've fucked that up.'

Spectacular.
Every government, for decades, eyes wide,
one step at a time, slid bayonet up the pub backside.
Cheaper to sit home drinking than come out?
Should be entirely the other way about, skewed thinking.
Pub drinking is the home of responsible drinking.
Learn how to drink but never twig you're being taught,
mature habits acquired with zero conscious thought.
In the natural run of things.
Circumstance not choice. Heaving understaffed bars, bog queues, stair, pub-to-pub stomps, via cash machines, other diversions – how long on an average night out drinking do you actually spend *without* a drink?

Fresh air, exercise, socialisation.

Whereas domestic drinking is pour lift swallow.

No waiting at bars.

Smoke on your arse.

Trudge to fridge, to bog, to door and back for takeaway you don't want, to sofa, to fridge, to sofa, to fridge, until you can't climb off your buttocks..

Crawl to pit.

Repeat to fade.

Bertram Russell reckoned every sesh was a little suicide and domestic consumption is the theory made flesh. But he was chatting absolute shit with regard to alcohol taken far from the safety of home and hearth.

The polar opposite of suicide.

A heightening of life.

A gauntlet self-flung down.

A vital bracing euphoric struggle.

Destroy, damage or otherwise impede your every faculty while tackling a series of random demanding mental and/or physical challenges.

Deal with complexity under the cosh of intoxication, order three Stella, two Guinness, a bottle of Newcy Brown, a pint and a half of Heineken Export, half with lime, a gin and tonic, a rum and coke and double scotch, then transport said fluids on a small wet tray or cradled in a web of splayed fingers, through a forest of writhing forms.

Successfully manage the visible effects of binged alcohol for long enough to pass a club bouncer or get a table at the Spice of Bengal.

Then, once you can barely see, negotiate the bus or train or tram network, or the taxi rank queue rife with every angry lairy scrapper who will not be getting his testes wet tonight.

A bumpy hell-ride with endless potential for disaster at every turn and no settled outcome at outset. By rights thousands should perish spectacularly amid the chaos every weekend.

Peel your pizza off that windscreen and remember where you live.

Sorry Bertram.

Get out.

You're rotting your liver on that settee.

But don't feel too bad. Same goes for me,

half the nights, average calendar month.
Maybe temporary suicide is what we crave.
Hard work, worry, regret, I – people get lonely,
end the farce for one night only.
Reborn next morn from pocket sprung grave,
to try again, fail again, fail etc.

'What did happen to your fucking face then?'

"I'll tell you. You ever been down Pigeon Street?"

Could be at home massaging my introduction.

Thinking about structure, research, establishing some point to it all.

Maybe it should be a novel. A proper novel like people like with plot and narrative.

People want stories again, whatever stories are.

I'll need to get a corkboard and some Post-its.

See my reflection in the bandit, just the side of Noel on the telephone on the features board, but only when the lights stop flashing.

There I am in that moment, half a peevish face, old and unrefined.

"I'm seeing this bird from Pigeon Street."

'Is she one of the people you could meet?'

"Eh?"

'Off the telly.'

"Who said she's off the telly?"

'Fuckin' Pigeon Street, fuck's sake, if you live on Pigeon Street, here are the people you could meet.'

A multicultural Trumpton for the times, with markedly lower production values.
No cunt lived in a windmill. Blacks were a thing. There was a female lorry driver who was probably a lesbian, and that's fine.

"Oh yeah yeah. Watch with Maggie…"

Half Man Half Biscuit wasn't about Trumpton they was about days of bad weed and kids TV when you should have had a job.

'I remember laughing at Pigeon Street when Eccy had digs over that end.'

"Oh aye… Was he in Albatross Street?"

'Yeah, they're all birds, the streets off that stretch, right down. There's a Parrot Street.'

"And Puffin, that's next over from her. You remember how fuckin' dank Eccy's was? They only had a Paki bog."

'Will you fuck off with that bollocks again? Anyhow them bogs are better for you, that's why we're all full of piles. We push too hard to shit because of prim Victorians.'

"Eccy reckoned he looked between his knees one time and was shitting straight onto a rat with its head up the hole."

'At least his bowels was proper open. Nobody outside the First World shits like us, like we're sat at a desk. They get down on it, open sesame, no pushing, no Farmers.'

I genuinely think nobody outside the First World has haemorrhoids.
Why?
Because I haven't looked it up.
Thick with rats that end of town.
Sliced by dead railway line, branches, tunnels to long gone mills.
Remember the track by the winter snake?
That running waking trauma dream?
The bird streets are at the head of that serpent.
Rats run the rails to reach them.
And pop-up in lavs on a whim.
Our rails are their roads, I've seen half a dozen trot single file through the station.

'Your lass on Pigeon Street got a squatter then? This romance could do wonders for your rectal health.'

"I'd shit in a sink first."

'Do you have piles?'

"Course I fuckin' do."

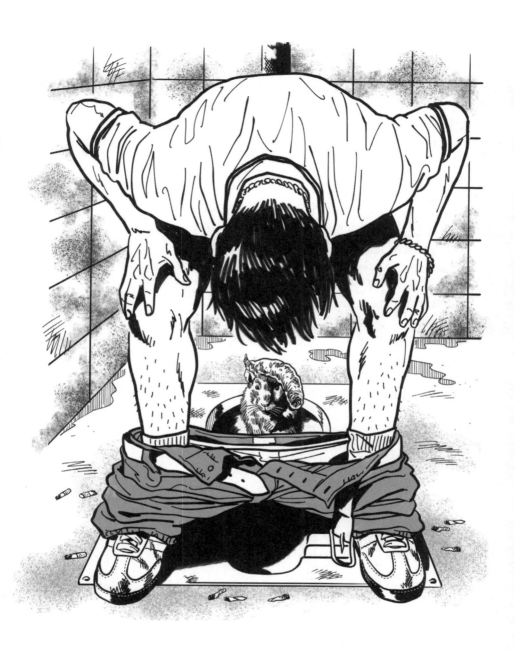

At least his bowels was proper open.

'I'm packing a backful. Internal thank fuck.'

"Yeah, I couldn't do with it if they were hanging out me arse."

Knew one lad had the set, upstairs, downstairs, inside, out,
could always tell when he was pressing the grapes of wrath.
He'd come a'mincing,
tiny soft steps,
sighing, wincing,
ooh-ah, eeeh, ooo...
You had to laugh.
Mine drop blood time to time.
Just long enough between bleeds so you forget for an instant and blanch in
your soul.
Always comes as a shock,
a bowl of fresh blood, until you remember.
First obviously the worst.
Didn't know I'd varicose veins
up my arse ready to burst.
Had a GP's digit on the job inside 20 minute, having insisted upon being seen
at once.
Threw panicked ab-dabs at front desk is the truth.
No-one fears death like the healthy stoned youth.
But most everyone suffers round the back, in the end.
And we suffer because we strain.
Go in the woods, tomorrow, pass rot in the great outdoor.
Free of porcelain throne you will naturally spurn sit up and beg,
and descend to haunches, chin to knee, lean into the leg,
hug those calves, gently flex and bingo, stress-free spoor.
A flock of sparrows.
Our body works.
We know this. Known for years. Yet we deny our kinship with beast of field
and shed, remain the hostages of mores and values long threadbare, dead,
of postern Puritanism. Grunting, squeezing, compressed apertures, vessels
busting, renting our soft tissues on angular dogma.

Cry Anusol for England, Harry and St George.

'I've shit all over this town. All over this country. I've shit on a volcano.'

"I've shit on a bus."

'Fuckin' hell. Why?'

"Had to, caught short. Caught it in my skidders and fegged 'em out the window. Going for a piss."

Running you get caught short plenty and there's no way round it nor time to make plans.
Not like piss.
Do ten miles full bladder no bother.
Far less when nature calls the other.
I've been right to the edge. I've been past the edge.
Last time fell foul went behind a council estate hedge.
A sprawling '50s sink on the outskirt, where the countryside begins.
Somehow made it to the furthest reach, pressed against privet alongside a narrow path and gurgling brook.
Distant dark fells bore mute witness to my urgent business, red lights on the TV antennae which tower at their summit twinkled through the rising gloom.
Next garden along, left, later glanced to spy,
a six-foot flag of St George, fluttering high.
Big red hand in the middle.
Next time, I thought. Next one's for you daddy.
A graveyard once, only once, no choice in the faecal matter, poo or die.
Vaulted the wall and without breaking stride
dropped shorts pressed myself close to the side,
into the cold stones, away from the laden earth.
Still don't feel great about it for what that's worth.

"There's these three Paki lads was always hanging round the shop down the corner of her road."

'How dare these bastards hang around parts of town where they live like we always did? Someone should round the fuckers up, gas some manners into 'em.'

"They're fuckin' dealers like, not bob-a-job."

'We weren't fucking scouts neither, and they're providing a public service then. We'd have been scoring off 'em 20 year ago.'

"Yeah, well, I was getting the piss ripped out of me off of 'em."

'Was they calling you a fat bastard?'

Going Underground, faint.
Tommo pulls a phone from inside pocket, Going Underground, loud.
Saaome people –
He speaks.

"Hello? Yeah, yeah, we've been fuckin' waitin' all – next the bandit."

Hangs up.

"He's here."

He turns, begins squinting at people in the pub.

'What you doing?'

"Looking for him."

'You ain't a clue what he looks like.'

"You Tommy?"

Oof what a catch.
Ratboy grew up.

Leaning in on the bandit side by Tommo's left shoulder and across, a squat scrote in an expensive three-quarter length black parka.

Maybe 40, not much either way. Clean-shaved dome, hard lean face a web of scar tissue old and new, ink teardrop, left hand on the table, pint in his right, beady eyes on me.

Seen this cutthroat before, hear a bell ring,

possibly in the dock when court reporting.

Or maybe a nightmare.

No, real. Different hair?

Didn't have raw SPAM so far as can place.

But did have them eyes, that cold grey gaze.

The Stanley tramline left ear to chin also new though, to me, not him. Fully healed but pink, acquired this decade maybe, sure I'd remember if seen.

Stitch that, a pro-job, two blades, matchstick in-between.

'Tommo? He is.'

"Where the fuck've you been?"

"My man wasn't there. He was picking up and I had to wait. Who the fuck is this cunt?"

A finger jabs my way.

Rude to point,

I think but don't say.

Wouldn't help anyone, least of all me.

"My mate, he's alright."

"Don't give a fuck what the cunt is, you got told you and me not you and yer fuckin' bum-chum."

"I-"

"Have you got the three hundred?"

"Yes."

Tommo pulls his wad.

"Not in here soppy cunt, up the side of the arc in five – fucking – minute."

Tommo firmly on the back foot in the space of 30 seconds and three sentences.
No wonder.
Here's a hardened criminal.
Anyone with eyes can tell
he'd put you in a coma
for the sake of merry hell.
His pale eyes rest on me and I say nothing, poker face it, nothing to see here
friend, forget about me.

"Five minutes."

"I'll come with you."

"No you fucking won't."

Puts the barely touched pint down and away, through the door, by the window,
gone.

'He seemed like a nice lad.'

"Give it a minute and we'll follow him."

'Give it five's what he said and think I'll give it a fucking hour. Tell you what,
I'll meet you in the Bull. Who the *fuck* is that hood?'

"Never met him, my mate put us onto a mate of his."

'Mate? That cunt ain't got no mates, just people he ain't stabbed yet.'

"Some fuckin' mate you."

'You don't need me holding your hand to score, you're a big boy now.'

"It ain't fuckin' coke!"

I believe him and wish that cocaine was what it could have been.
Bored and a bad feeling, be delighted to bail.
But bound forever, as discussed in some detail.
We wriggled on a floor, stopped kicks together one night in the 1980s, he washed blood out of my hair and ear in the bus station bogs.

'I'll stand at the corner, but fucked if I'm giving that *playa* a look at my face.'

"He's seen you once already."

'I'll stick at once if it's best going.'

"Has that been five minutes?"

'No idea, I'm half-pissed.'

Four or five Stella swift is felt, lately,
from boots to bald-spot, tolerance lame.
Consciously crippled, telling it rightly.
I've cut back. Stopped working the same.
Still good in the moment,
in one's cups, but mood precarious
and frequently led down various
long dead-ends off memory lane,
nudged by a name, a taste, a lament.
Tours of things never to be set right again.
And the hangovers are a different pain.
Less physical more mental.
Never used to cry and want to die.

I get down in myself, like the man said.
I get down and think about quitting,
but worry what I'd do with my hands of an evening.
Remember, winter is almost here and men my age top themselves for fun.
And younger. Poor Wedge.
So find and hold the balance, slow it down.
Jump on bitter in the Bull, sit out a round.

"That *must* be five minutes, come on."

'Fuck! I'm having a piss.'

16

Here we are then.

Tower of power, heady font of the Saracen's subterranean centuries of mass piss.

The tangy musk of mature urea registers momentarily upon entry but swiftly hides herself beneath a veil of Toilet Duck and trough-cake.

Oh yes she is a woman.

And it is a trough.

An open trough, no dividers.

Not a fan of the open trough.

Not at the best of times.

And this moment, in this pub, is far from that.

One of the first things lost to a drunk is spatial awareness.

Happily squidge into spaces don't exist, aim careless,

jet their carefree wandering wee-wees

over your smart new tan suede Wallabees.

A urinal gives even the pissedest cunt an aim in life. A point of focus, a clear goal, boundaries, a sense of ownership.

Got three lads on the go at a four yard trough, evenly distributed.

There's a space foot and half could maybe squeeze into between the bloater in the middle with a crease in the back of his head and the slighter Peaky Blinder on his left, but really don't fancy it.

Couldn't enjoy the piss thinking about my shoes.

Fabric uppers. Straight through to sock.

Oi piss-toes!

One cubicle, closed, silent, obvious user,

get a snort on you Class A loser.

Oh aye, I'll go cubicle and take all that entails.

At my age do I care if strangers dub me Shy-cock Holmes?

Sniff up twat, let an old man drain his balls.

If there was a queue I'd risk one in the basin, no bones.

Always a nervy tactic off trusted turf. Only needs one of these pissers to be a

Not a fan of the open trough.

regular, a friend of the landlord, the barman's brother, take your pick, casual glance over the shoulder, next I'm explaining myself half-cut, dick out, to some shitfaced thickwit who has no reason to like me nor to invest the time necessary to find out we might have a lot in common and that I am, broadly speaking, on his side.

"Who in fuck d'you think you are pissing in that sink?"

'I'm a distinctive working class literary voice mate, trying to capture and communicate something true, in a form which although superficially stylised is in fact a hyper-realisti –'

Bang, and I'm down and wriggling
in the piss of ages, cock still trickling.

"My sister or brother or mate owns this pub you cunt, she's just about hanging on. Had to let the cleaners go, she scrubs those sinks herself, get to fuck you're on my side."

And in goes the boot and I'd deserve it.
Don't even have a sister but the thought of some jumped-up hack no mark slashing over her efforts, her work, her dreams, their piss on her imagined skin, boils my blood.
Look at that grout. Spider's web of hairline cracks and lesser erosion borders every tile, drinking down the fresh piddle, exuding the ancient miasma.
Christ is Dickens piss on the air?
Am I breathing long decayed atoms of that man's libidinal essences?
What a lovely thought.
Dying. That's the weed. You can sit unawares for hours until you stand up and find you've a space hopper bladder stoppered one millimetre behind your Jap's eye.
Space at the trough, thank God, thank God, it's the fat cunt too, so a bit of elbow room.
Eyes front, come on.
Come on you're there.

Come on.

Spent a grim few minutes pressing a piss in the Queen's Head, Monday, nearly turned it in from sheer embarrassment. Then got in the flow with a fart loud as tearing carpet.

Prostate? Don't think so. Psychological. Only ever when I've had to wait and think.

Feedback loop. Once crosses the mind how awkward it is not being able to piss for long periods in front of strange men then lo and behold, your vicious self is up for a laugh.

Did I think about the Queen's Head incident just now? Don't recall. Is a fart gumming up the works? Be careful there though. If in doubt, sit it out.

Better a seated piss than a standing shite.

I'll be alright if he washes his hands, a running tap usually –

You dirty sod.

Come on.

Water. A hosepipe. A stream, darting, bubbling. A narrow river full of sunshine sparkles, rippling over pebbles. Rushing through a forest. We descend from path to bank, to sit beneath a tree, on a large smooth rock overlooking a small waterfall, the breeze stirs the leaves as it does her golden hair. Is that ten years ago? Try 20. She turns and speaks but the white noise water washes away her words so you move closer, watch her soft pink lips shape words you cannot hear, and the water –

Whoooooooosshhhhh...

Sweet release.

Saved by the flush.

Where was that day?

The river widened, gained weight, the banks steepened and trees gave way to pylons, open empty fields.

The path faded and we turned back.

17

"Is that him, down there, that car?"

Halfway along the narrow street between the arcade and the precinct, in the shadow between two pools of streetlight, a hatchback ticks over, softly fumes. Wayne squints.

"Is that a car?"

'Are you fucking blind or what? Course it's a car.'

"Is it him?'

'Parked where he said to head.'

"Come down with us a bit."

'I'm better here mate, only wound him up before didn't I? If it kicks-off I'll shout for help while I'm running over to the Bull.'

"You're not running anywhere cripple."

'Go on, shift your arse. It's raining, getting pissed on here. Am watching your back.'

And'll definitely shout for help while running over to the Bull.
I can limp fast in short bursts after a drink.
Tssshhh, nothing's kicking off.
Why would anything kick-off? My presence aside is all as planned, a straightforward mysterious transaction down an alley.
He'll get what he's after then we'll both toddle the Bull.
I'll show him the caricature of Dickens with 'penis' in his beard and explain

why that will be the cover of the book.

Actually no I won't. Don't bring up the book again, can't be arsed.

Nye already knows about it, might mention it, none of the rest will give a fuck.

Get through this then forget the present, dive straight into the lovely past.

Why begrudge ourselves? Our journey is nearly over, at last.

Just remember keep it light.

One started crying one night.

Said he wished we were kids again,

how he wanted to go back,

wanted to tell him he was insane.

Angered but tempered with pity,

quelled urge to slap and shake the dope,

tell him I love him but there is no hope.

Me too, I lied, never having entertained such a futile worldview,

laying in good will against the inevitable day that I break, and do.

Why is Tommo getting *in* the fucking car?

What's he buying entails doing that?

The car?

What the fuck is he into here?

Definitely believe him about the powder.

Nobody scoring coke by the three-ton-load can sit in a pub for two hours and avoid talking about themselves, and it has been a taciturn Tommo tonight.

Two hours of conversation and no clue where he lives, what he's doing, what he has been doing, nothing.

All learned for sure is that he's now a conscious racist rather than a reflex one and that he is, like I, alone.

Bar this bird on Pigeon Street.

"Scuse me asking have you got 52p please? Trying get back to Blackburn."

Fuck. Him again.

'Nah sorry mate. Look I'll be honest with you, I'm broke.'

"You're out on the piss."

Cheeky bastard. Yeah I am out on the piss, I've ate beans all week to afford it.

'I just ain't got no spare, che.'

"I need 52p get back to Blackburn."

Always need get somewhere and a specific sum.
Few you see every day work the same spots,
in and around the stations and the bus stops,
shy X amount, to get back from whence come.

'I can't help you mate. I'll be another week on the ALDI beans after this, I'm fuckin' skint. Do you want a fag?'

"Yeah."

The gift of fag a decent fallback in straitened times, as ever.
A fag is a truly comradely gesture. Value to them, value to you, and they know it has value to you, know that's a fag you won't be smoking. What do non-smokers have to offer other than the wads of money they save on fags?
A toffee?
Actually I'd take a toffee most times and be glad of it.

'Get a bad press these days, fags, just because they're lethal.'

Life is a lethal pursuit and we are the quarry, sorry.

"I only have the odd one."

'Best way, just thinking that before. A light habit might kill you but if you keep an eye on the lard and drag your arse off the sofa now and then you can count yourself unlucky.'

And plenty are unlucky too.
But below the headline figure.

Which ain't to say it won't end you.
Weigh the odds place your bets.
How much do you like cigarettes?
How long do you wish to stay?
Last orders half past ten.

"I don't have a sofa."

'Course you ain't, best way.'

Like most pleasures with potential to do harm you must respect the
vice.
Sofas.
Coca Cola is pure poison but a blob in rum is nice.
And the odd one now and then means the shite could be ten times *worse* for
human health and still you'd be golden.
But swill three litre a day and it'll put you in the ground sure as a Benny
Hedgehog habit.

'Roll your own?'

"Ta."

'That enough?'

"Ta."

'Minty filter?'

"No ta."

'Dot Cotton.'

"Eh?"

Too young.

'What's in Blackburn?'

"Eh?"

'You can't get back to Blackburn.'

"I ain't going Blackburn, have you got a light?"

Couldn't put an age on the face illuminated by Clipper's glow.
They age fast in the elements. Full-on winter two month or so.
And a taste already in these icy raindrops.

"Where's your mate?"

'Down there up to no good.'

"Tell him he's a cunt."

'Ahhh, he knows.'

Hard to argue with that assessment.
Behind me an engine starts, a car door slams, and I turn half-expecting to see
Tommo in a steaming hump on the pavement, throat cut, gurgling not able to
scream.
But instead he's walking quickly our way.

'Sorted?'

"Fuck off you scruffy cunt or I'll knock you out."

"Your mate give us a fag."

"Well fuck off and smoke it!"

Token lunge enough to send the poor rag on his way.

"What'd you give him a fag for?"

'What do you act like a twat for? Everything sorted then? Are we done here?'

"What time is it?"

'Half-nine?'

"Let's get a taxi."

'Do fuck off, it's a ten minute walk.'

"Is pissing down."

'That be why we're getting wet, come on.'

Not taken ten steps before my hip penetrates the Stella to tell me how much it enjoys the cold and damp.

'This fucking hip.'

"Wish you was in a nice warm taxi now Uncle Albert?"

'The fucking rank's near far as the Bull.'

"I'll call and we can wait in the Saracen's."

'I'd happier drown than go back in there.'

"So stop moaning granddad."

'I'll show you that Dickens thing on the wall at the Bull.'

"That what thing?"

Actually, remember, will not show him that Dickens thing nor for that matter mention the book again tonight.

'Nothing, you got sorted then?

"Aye."

'Where is it?'

"Where's what?"

'Your three hundred quid worth?'

Catch his eye, and spy someone I ain't seen in 40 years. The daft kid met late 70s, wheeling a tenth-hand Tomahawk round the top rec.
That's right, Tommo, Tomahawk. You don't know his name. Rode that bike until he was a teenage gangler kneeing himself in the face every pedal, until Tommo stuck.
And there is that boy, peeping through a mask now old and meaty.
Know that exact expression. Seen it plenty back in the day.
Glimpsed it across a sprung dancefloor between swinging legs.
Shitting his self.

"It's in that fucking car."

18

The hip croons a shrill siren song.
Water invaded one shoe
and the other before long.
Then squeaking sock too.

"Thing is, I didn't give a shit, I wasn't fucking arsed, then one of the little cunts
starts shouting Masterchef every time I go past, every fucking time."

'One of what little cunts?'

"Them pakis down the shop in Pigeon –"

'Fuck me that paki shit's getting dull. I'm on the piss with a senile cabbie
UKIP cunt.'

It does get boring,
forgiving, ignoring.

"I couldn't give a shit! Fuck 'em, they started it, am I meant to be made a cunt
of in front of my bird by some bit of a fuckin' kid?"

'Why Masterchef?'

"When I'm wearing glasses."

'You don't wear glasses.'

"I ain't going to come out in 'em."

Very wise.
I'd have ripped piss on sight,

then non-stop all night.

Don't buy into the widespread myth that because more people wear glasses now it is somehow less pissripworthy. Styles to suit every Magoo, oooh they're rimless, it isn't like you're wearing specs at all.

Oh yes it is four-eyes.

A fairytale propagated by Specsavers to shift more specs.

Stop wanking Joe 90 you'll need a labrador next.

Now every third kid and second adult boggles through goggles.

Have human eyes got worse or spectacle salesman got better?

Ask an optician but – word to the wise – don't expect them to blow the scam.

From juniors right through high school there was one kid under glass in my class.

One poor ragged bullied teased jam-jar; yours truly in case you can't guess.

Bespectacled 'til late teens, lenses thick, profound short sight, so tiny weenie rat eyes. From the age of 4 or 5, right up until contacts came cheaper and a set for my big 18th.

Just the one fat lad too. Fat Billy.

One. Seen it now? Getting silly.

Often times, ashamed to say, threw Billy under the bus to save myself.

Gave the hounds his scent.

'Big fat Billy had a one-inch willy and he showed it to the girl next door! She thought it was a pea so she had it for her tea, now fat Billy has no willy any more!'

A two-bladed Stanley wound for Billy as he did indeed have a very small penis.

Showers after PE. Hell for some.

Now the catbird seat is mine.

Me, with the advanced macular degeneration

which will leave me blind.

Someone has to pay, and my quiver of revenge bristles with tried and tested mockery.

Tried and tested on me.

Now I sing Steamy Windows when you fog-up in hot chip-shops.

'What'd they mean Masterchef?'

Often times, ashamed to say, threw Billy under the bus to save myself.

"That Greg fucker off it."

Quality lateral pisstaking, the thick baked-bean thumbhead and stub neck.

'You'll have to change your frames or grow your hair back.'

This not of course an option.
Long cropped, not choice.
Tommo's loss began early,
but he baulked at action.
Hung on to his flick,
so we staged an intervention.
Mate, you look a dick
like Bobby Charlton.
We all need that friendly voice.

'You'd've been Mr Whippy for years if it ain't been for us, Masterchef ain't so bad.'

"Aye, well, he wasn't so cocky without his mates."

And a door swings open and the room beyond is darkness.

'How'd you mean?'

"I seen him on his on his bike on his Jones a few week back."

'Aww, what the fuck you done?'

Never ask a question when you know the answer and'd sooner it not be confirmed.

'I don't want to know.'

He stops walking and looks at me.

The faded bruises show darker on skin bleached by LED streetlights.
He's furious, spitting words.

"What would *you* have done? Eh? Have fucking bits of kids playing gangster shiting you every time you need a pint of milk or 20 fags?"

'Just 'cos you're seeing a lass down the road don't mean you have to move your weekly shop to her local Booz n Nooz.'

"She never has fuck all in, she's nuts! But you, what, you'd've walked half an hour to North Road, got your fags there, would you?"

'I'd have not risen to it. I'm a 50 year old man, so are you.'

I'd have raged impotent.
And maybe limped.
Raged limpotent to North Road.
We walk on, quicker.

"Give him a few fucking digs haven't I? Less than what he was due."

'Don't tell me.'

"Nothing, three or four slaps. Should've give him more."

'Or left alone.'

"I nudged him off his bike with the car."

'You fucking maniac.'

"I only bumped him, back wheel, he should have left it there."

'Yeah, but then, of course, we wouldn't have.'

"We might have, we never got them lads back who twatted us that do that night."

'Yeah, cos they were all five year older, *proper fucking headcases*, and we knew it'd come back on us ten times worse.'

"I never thought this would."

'Is that where your face is from?'

"Dropped on us mob-handed, cunts, on my back locking the car."

'You fucking idiot.'

"I hears this shout then it all went black. They'd been up the lobby side of hers."

'Did they shout Masterchef?'

"Ha ha, very funny that. Got fucking scraped off the pavement in the back of an ambulance, mate, hospital overnight."

'Police collar them?'

"*Police?* Have they fuck. Pig in hospital an hour that night asking questions while I'm fucking concussed is last I've heard."

'Did you tell 'em about the lad you twatted?'

"A split lip ain't a twatting."

'Alright, run over in your car.'

"Fucking nudged his back wheel about 15 mile an hour, I didn't wind the cunt round me axle. Didn't even knee his jeans."

'You told 'em though.'

"And have me get fuckin' nicked? Did I fuck as like, how would that help?"

Fair point. That's right, officer, I believe a teenage boy driven off his bicycle and violently assaulted by myself some weeks ago might be nursing a vendetta.

"Two teeth gone this side. Fractured fuckin' cheekbone."

He stops again, points at a faint purple crescent below and slightly right of his left eye.

"One centimetre up, that, I'd have lost this fucker, I'd have a fuckin' marble in there like Twateye."

Poor Twateye. He'd an eye gone. The lids over empty socket looked like a vagina.
See?
Kids are hard.
Be less grief for the four-eyed these days,
double-glazed tots too commonplace,
and you'd expect obesity benefits from ubiquity.
Dollops dying under the literal weight of gullibility over what is and is not a treat and when a treat is or is not valid.
Not their fault, much confusion
around rewards and consolation.
But children always tease,
they mean no harm, is nature.
A phase which passes quickly in most cases,
although the President of America
mocks cripples and abuses certain races.
Wanky tech skills probably earn you a stinging nickname to carry through life now.
I don't know. I'll never know. No kids. Their world might as well be Mars.

'Who come up with Twateye?'

"Wayne."

'Vicious little bastard.'

"I don't think he minded, Twateye. By the end he'd answer to it."

'Nah nah, never fall for that. Pretending you don't mind oldest trick in the book.'

A book I owned from age 7, from when first walked out of an opticians with
coke-bottle bottoms clipped to my face.
And played that trick too,
mostly worked, only the guileful saw through.
If not maybe Billy happened by for me to transfer the cross.

"He was some snooker player though wasn't he?"

'Twateye? Wouldn't have thought so.'

"Wayne."

'Oh aye, could've gone pro.'

He was a pro-tormentor.
Wound people up like he could reach out and turn a key in their forehead, big
smile on his face, all pleasant and affable.
A seven-stone ferret and master of tone and phrase, spry, agile, always a step
out of punch range, probing, and if spied so much as a solitary nerve flicker in
a cheek at a certain word or phrase, he had you.
He knew.
You *mind* that, don't you?

"Never seen nobody smack 'em in the middle like that from them angles in
real life."

'Cue was bigger than him when I first seen him play. Smashed some greasy slob old club player with silver hair like a shop steward on the league table by the bar.'

Brylcreamed, slicked back flat the colour of mercury.

"Wonder how come he never went pro?"

'He went alkie instead. Lushed up before he was 20, sleeping rough. Tony seen him in a fucking tent down the woods one year.'

"Daft bastard."

'He could have been the next Tony Meo.'

"The Rocket."

'Nah, he wasn't that good. So what is in that fucking car then?'

"The lad. From the Saracen's."

'What'd he give you?'

"It's what I give him."

'Three hundred quid.'

"And the rest."

'You said you had three hundred.'

"Give my mate three hundred to give his mate to give him last week."

'You've give that scrote six hundred quid?'

"Yeah. And an address."

19

Someone knocking at the door.
Somebody ringing the bell.
Someone knocking at the door.
Somebody ringing the bell.
Do me a favour.
Secure the door.
Don't let 'em in.
Call the police.

"It's the ringleader, this bastard."

'Don't want to know another thing, this is fucking heavy.'

"Big fucker, older than the others, he was the boss. Never said a word at the shop, just laughing."

'Good for him, don't say another word.'

"Katy clocked him."

'Katy?'

"The Pigeon Street bird. He was going in an house behind where the GEM used to be."

'We went there, first big supermarket round here.'

"I drove round them streets a bit, hung about, and it fuckin' was."

'Massive that mill. Wide aisles. Never seen a supermarket before except on the telly. Me and our kid nicked trolleys and raced 'em. Everyone did, free karties.

There wasn't a hedge that side of town didn't have a trolley stuffed in it.'

"This fucker wanted a grand first, but my mate owes me, got his mate to talk him down."

'Mates' rates all round, change the subject.'

That murderer seen me,
had a good long look.
So now I have a stake,
if he's brought to book.
Hang on.

'This is the only reason you're even fuckin' out tonight ain't it?'

"Eh?"

'Get out and about, be seen, so when the kid you twatted gets pulled in and asked if his mate had any enemies the prime suspect will be on cameras all over town.'

"He won't be."

'Of course he fucking will! Did your mate have any enemies son? Oh right, Pigeon Street you say? Which house? Can you point out Masterchef?'

We stump on in silence, squelching.
I sorely, if not stumbling,
He head low, grumbling,
as always once rumbled.
Bang to rights, tumbled.
From juvenile vandalism circa 1978 to conspiracy to murder 2019.

"I rung Nye before I knew about tonight."

Everyone did, free karties.

'Then booked The Poundland Jackal to fit. Was it your bright idea to meet the cunt in a crowded pub?'

"His, my mate said his mate'd said he'd said it was safer."

'Suppose it is for him, cos if nothing else he's tied his self to you in a public place, front of witnesses.'

And to me.

'Fuck alone knows how many people seen us with him tonight.'

"Nobody was looking at us."

'How the fuck do you know? Be CCTV in the Saracen's any road I bet, probably a condition of the licence, stop 'em all glassing each other to fuck. He'd a pint, maybe chat the landlord a bit so he'd be remembered. Quick natter with his pals then off to business, pint untouched, chased moments later by the defendants, your Honour.'

Footage viewed in court.
Tits deep in his mess.
Skin in the game, as it were.
Best wish the killer success
on his ghastly endeavour.

"Don't be fuckin' paranoid, that's blowing half your life on weed."

'It ain't paranoia when fuckers will definitely be out to get you.'

"Nobody is out to get you."

'They will be once your hit-chav fucks up gets nicked and starts squawking.'

"Why would he fuck up?"

'Why wouldn't he? Did your mate's mate run him through compare the market dotcom?'

"He reckoned he's done at least two he knows of."

'*Simples!*'

"Eh?"

'Them fucking meerkats!'

Fucking *hate* them meerkats.

20

The Bull.
The heaving Bull.
Loud shit music.
Where Dickens laid his head down,
dreamed of Coketown, this town,
commemorated on wall in lobby,
'penis' beard, could be anybody.

"It's fuckin' rammed."

'If they ain't got a table I am out of here, my hip is gonna explode.'

"Eh? What do you want?"

'To collapse and die.'

The learning curve I joined upon diagnosis steepens every day.
This ruined joint has gained a loud and nagging voice
which will be heard and heeded lest a dreadful price to pay.
And as winter dawns, it tells me loud and clear,
getting wet and cold lights a fucking fire in here.
Getting to know you, getting to know all about you.
We've only just beguuuun... to limp...

"To drink, going bar."

'A short. Rum. Double cheapest and ice. Serious, if they ain't got a table I'll neck it and-'

He turns, presses his sodden self upon the glut of hot bodies three or four deep about the clamouring bar, and is gone.

'Penis' beard, could be anybody.

Crosses my mind to walk out and home via Tesco Express for a bottle, red, a
selection of salty snacks, a consoling Twix.
Beer then wine, that'll be fine,
be rained sober by the time
I get back, a hot shower,
dry sock, skin-up, cork out,
life richer for the pourer.
Copyright Bargain Booze.
A Bertram Russell night in then away to empty bed,
alone with my respiration, considering masturbation,
not thinking about that car at its destination,
in shadow in sight of the door. Unless he's already dead.
Maybe it's already done.
I'll stay. To see the old lot one last time before getting sent to prison where I
will die.
If and only if they've got a fucking table.
Can't stand in this scrum, leg too unstable.
Young meat in motion, hands toting glasses.
Big loud lads full of blood, full of beards,
diving about to impress the lasses.
Heartening to see nothing has changed,
heartbreaking to be a ghost at their feast.
We are murderous wallpaper.

"Barney."

I'd be jealous were there any point.
Tonight they make memories not chew and be chewed by the past.
Although my evening too will be remembered,
spoken of down the road.
Quite possibly under oath.

"Barney."

So help me God.

"Barney?"

'Nye, mate, miles off, miles off there. How goes?'

"Not bad mate. Still wet out?"

'Fuckin' right – where we sat?'

"There's only me. No tables."

'I thought Kecks was already out.'

"Nah, just texted, his lass has flu."

'I thought him and Butch was coming with you?'

"Butch was but he cried off this affs, working tomorrow."

'Heard from Pete?'

"Nah but he might be on the train."

'Dan?'

"I emailed him when it was and he said probably but I haven't heard since..."

'Mick?'

"PortAventura."

'Jammy fuckin' bastard.'

Imagine being hot and dry.

"Where's Tommo?"

'At the bar.'

"How is he?"

'Same as ever. Worse than ever. Don't ask about his fuckin' face.'

In fact Nye fuck off now before he gets served, before he's here, before you get called as a witness, dragged in as co-conspirator.
Go home to your family and I'll limp back to my empty flat and we'll pretend nothing ever happened.

"Sorry about fucking off the Saracens before, Liam was late kicking off, then they was fucking about after…"

'No worries, I wish I had. How's Sally and the little 'un?'

"Good mate, aye. Richard's not so little now though. Started school this time if you can believe."

'Fuckin' hell, time eh?'

"You should come round for tea one night, Sal keeps saying she'd love to see y'."

'I keep meaning to.'

It's been years. I'm envious of all he has that I do not.

"You still running?"

Am I still running?

'No mate, bit of a bummer, doctors reckon I won't run again.'

"Aww, bollocks. Sad to hear that mate."

'Yeah, and if I could run I'd be running now. Out that fucking door and across this town.'

I grip his right arm and a few drops of his Guinness splash on my sleeve.

'There's a hole in my life mate. I've run every morning, hardly ever missed, coming up 20 year. Out of bed early, stretching, striding, downing coffee until I've emptied my back then off, every season, through weather you wouldn't throw a dead fucking dog out in. Brutalising myself for the hour or so of inner peace that comes when I stop.'

Nye nods, makes a sympathetic sound.

'I turned a corner and saw a man hitting himself on the top of his head with a hammer. Bang bang bang he goes then stops and sighs, big smile on his face. Then bang bang bang and repeat. I goes why you twatting yourself in the head with a hammer? He goes because it feels sooo good when I stop.'

A girl laughs right in my ear.

'I know every fucking millimetre of this town, Nye, centre to edge, leafy rich and cut-off poor alike. Avenues plush and harsh, smooth tarmac and ploughed asphalt, of green breadth and honey stone, failing concrete and grit.'

Avenues of ancient tree and topiary not bowed picket fence and barking mongrel.
The avenues, drives, closes which constitute this town's twatted estates were not named at outset in a spirit of mockery, not when smart and well-maintained, but now are nothing less, in their deepening regress.
Nye glances down at my gripping hand, frowns, transfers the stout to his left hand.

'Every day I crossed the heart of this town, Nye, lost myself in the broken heart, red terrace veins there converging, encircling salvaged mills and ghosts of mills as ants dance about the Queen. The arteries of this town's retail offer and night-time economy, the vacancies and bookies, charity shops and white elephants. British Homes Stores is home to the homeless now, Nye. Where your granny and mine got their bedding, those big wide doors are digs for dossers, 5 or 6 always, safer on the High Street, better lit, passing coppers. It's in the backs and alleys the poor cunts get set on fire.'

Nye's half-hearted attempt to break my grip merely spurs it to tighten, knuckles whiten.

'Did you know the council wants those doors boarded over? The dregs spoil the retail quarter experience, but the landlord ain't playing ball. Do you know how many quarters there is in this town now? Restaurant quarter, creative quarter, business quarter, there's five or six quarters. The takeaway quarter, greasy running, kerb skittery with thigh bones and wax, the stabbing quarter, the market quarter, dodging vans, swerving shift workers, all-night drinkers, dirty stop-outs, slinking home stinking, rubbing their eyes and yawning. Then to a park, to all the parks, but always my park, the park by the river, where the estuary air is fresh and you find yourself anew and watch the squirrels.'

Nye breaks free, takes a step back, and I almost fall forward in my haste to keep hold, seizing his lapels in both hands, slumping my bodyweight against him. A space clears about us, conversation falls off, there is a guffaw, I begin to shout. Scream.

'Fuck you child, you'll learn! Four months dark, four months light, four months spring and autumn, out beneath all the stars, home beneath the one. I saw every moon wax and wane, come, go, alone, silent, rhythmic, heart thumping, lungs pumping, eyes wide open on the never-reached horizon. It's all gone, Nye, my only escape.'

Silence. The pub is silence.

"Barney?"

The hubbub.

'Mm?'

"I said, you still running mate?"

'Oh, I...'

"You alright mate? You've gone grey."

'Yeah, no, not for a few month now. Me hip's fucked. I thought I'd seen you since...'

"Nah. How long's it going to take to mend?"

'Never, is for good. Should have cut back five year ago they reckoned, but I was poppin' fuckin' pills...'

There are no drops of stout on my sleeve.

"Get a bike."

'Not the same.'

Cycling is bourgeois, I'm flat broke.
Buy a bike? Couldn't run to a spoke.

"How's the book going?"

'Like cold shit. Sold ten copies last week, made me all of thirty quid.'

"Is that the one about piss?"

'Eh? Oh, no, no, the first one. Fucked that piss one off. The next is that thing I mentioned about Coketown.'

"Coketown?"

'Preston. Hard times, Dickens. Memories, murders. Pasts we can't face, shit gets forgot. Toxic masculinity. All sorts, it's vague.'

"How's it going?"

Here comes Tommo.

'Going? It's finished.'